THOUGH HE SLAY ME

Our Experience with Lewy Body Dementia

Anne Hartman

To Kathy,
With love,
Anne Hartman

xulon PRESS

Though he slay me,

I will hope in him...

JOB 13:15A

Your eyes saw my unformed substance;

in your book were written, every one of them,

the days that were formed for me,

when as yet there were none of them.

PSALMS 139:16

To our family at

Franklin Heights Baptist Church,

Rocky Mount, Va.

Contents

Preface

This book is a journal I kept for three years as my husband John and I went through his diagnosed time with Lewy Body dementia. When we learned that he had this disease, we dedicated the disease and our walk through it to the Lord, knowing He could use it to His glory. I pray that this book will help other care-givers as they walk through this valley of the shadow of death, and will fear no evil. The writing is just as written in my journals, i.e., incomplete sentences, hurried, and at times, frustrated!

ANNE HARTMAN

April 2010

Introduction

I guess I should have known something was wrong when John started having night episodes, talking incoherently, jumping up and walking around the house, as if he were looking for something. These began back in the 90s, but were infrequent enough that I just thought his work was affecting him. They became more frequent after retiring, however, and I was concerned, but still assumed he had had a hard day when they occurred.

I guess I should have known something was wrong when he forgot how to sail. He had been a great captain of several different boats on Lake Erie, but after we got a 16-foot sailboat for Smith Mountain Lake, he could no longer sail it. I did not know what was wrong, just thought maybe the smaller boat was harder to control.

I guess I should have known something was wrong when he nearly sawed off his thumb in June 2004, doing work in his carpentry shop like he had done for years.

I guess I should have known something was wrong when we were putting together a simple garage shelf in 2005, and he seemed to not know how to do it, even with instructions.

And when we were living with Susan and Roger, and I would volunteer him to help them with a project, and he seemed reluctant to help. I realized later that he probably did not know how to do what was needed.

When his friend Bob came over to help him build a fence for the pasture behind our house, Bob could see something was not right. He told Betty to insist that I get John to a doctor for testing. He noticed that John did not seem to know what he was doing. Betty told me, and eventually I made an appointment for him with Dr. A, our General Physician, who referred him to a neurologist in Roanoke.

We went to Dr. T, who talked to both of us, examined John, and referred John to another neurologist, who gave John hours and hours of testing, and both of these doctors came up with the diagnosis of probable Lewy Body dementia. At that time, they called it mild cognitive disorder, or early-onset dementia. John was diagnosed in July 2006 as we were building our house. Both of us believe in the Sovereignty of God, and we dedicated this illness and our response to it to God, for His glory. I was not keeping a journal in 2006, but I began in November of that year. The following chapters are the contents of the journal.

Moving on with life

12.21.06   John had a rough night last night—ergo: so did I!
He doesn't even remember—thought he slept through the night.
He was up four times to use the bathroom; went in wrong direction
twice. Also up once pulling the sheets and blankets off at the end
of bed "to get in." I told him to put his head on his pillow and get
in that way. He always goes back to sleep, then doesn't remember
it the next morning. I have a hard time falling back to sleep. We
went to Dr. T Tuesday morning; John told him all the projects he
has been doing, and Dr. T was surprised and praised him, puzzling
about his diagnosis of LBD. Reiterated the diagnosis of mild cognitive impairment, gave him samples of Aricept, and we are to come
back in six months.

Then Dr. T called after further reviewing the records, and said he wanted John to have an EEG—that the "episodes" in the night may be seizures. That is set for January 9–10. At times, I don't think about his dementia; everything seems normal. Then when we try to discuss something or just plain communicate in normal conversation, I realize what a problem he has. There are no subtleties, no "quick on the uptake" repartee; but then, there never was that kind of conversation between us... God, give me the Holy Spirit's patience and love...

12.31.06   A wonderful Christmas in Ohio with the Ewans; upon returning, we faced the death of Bob, a friend of over 40 years. Praise God that we know Bob is with Him. We welcomed the new year with the Swartzes and Betty—none of us could remember if this was our 4th or 5th New Year together. We all missed Bob, but are thankful that he is with the Lord. Grace's tumor marker is up to 1,000, so we continue to pray for her health, even as we wonder if she will be bringing in the next new year with us.

01.08.07   Betty and I are talking about going hiking on a trip. I wonder about going off to hike with friends and leaving John. I wish he had a good friend to do things with. I am struggling with my attitude toward him these days: we are having hard times conversing; he doesn't respond, or doesn't make sense sometimes then he does respond. I need more patience and more love. I pray that the upcoming EEG will help doctors know more about what is going on...

01.15.07   John has not had another night episode, so far as I can tell. He leaves our bed in the middle of the night, so he may be having them, and I don't hear him. I pray he will have one Wednesday night while the EEG is hooked to his head.

01.19.07   My Renovaré goal for this week is to watch my tongue: to only speak when necessary and edifying. Well, I blew it in a conversation with Cheri about Mother. God, forgive me. Then a much worse sin when I became upset with John yesterday. He was making coffee, standing by the coffee maker. I realized too late that he forgot to put the carafe under the spout! Coffee went everywhere when it started brewing. Mess! Sometimes I just want to not be here! (in the house!)

Took John to neurologist to unhook John; Dr. T said he was hoping for a different diagnosis that will be treatable.

01.23.07   Well, we just got a call from Dr. T's office: EEG was normal, i.e., did not show any seizures having taken place. So we are back to the original diagnosis: MCI, mild cognitive impairment, which may or may not get worse. He did have four more episodes: once got up and went to bedroom's french doors, talking and looking outside on to the porch as if looking for someone. Other three were just strong body jerks, waking me up, once he yelled loudly. After a few tears that the outcome of EEG was not going to help us, we prayed together for strength to face "whatever." **03.01.07** How did five weeks go by so quickly?! John seems to be doing much better. The weekend in Columbus was nice; he seemed normal all the time. Still having "lapses" in conversation; reads more slowly, misses words; night episodes not as frequent nor as violent. Praise God! For some reason, my "self" is needing attention; I am struggling again with humility, or lack of! Twice recently I have got upset with close friends and behaved "icily", not sure either one noticed. Silly reaction from me, and I am bringing it to the Lord and not discussing it with anyone. One reaction in both cases was to back off from the friendship—then wondered if I was over-extended and possibly looking for a way to get out of some friendship obligations?! But I love both too much to drop them. I am spending a lot of time with church-related work, i.e., church clerk duties, women's ministry budget, also Free Clinic board work is taking much time. My assignment this week for Renovaré is to write a letter to God; so here goes:

Dear God,

I am trying to remember the first time I sensed your presence. Since I gave my life to You at seven years old, it is hard to remember... . I think what I remember most is that I sensed that I was special to You. I recognized You were aware of me and my feelings, and I wanted so much to please You. My choice of John as my husband was a reflection of my wanting to serve You as a Christian homemaker. Even when I was disobedient and looking for my own pleasures and edification, I sensed Your presence in my life, drawing me back to You.

I remember times of absolute peace sitting in worship services, not even remembering the music or the message. I remember You speaking to me in the words of two contemporary songs: "Can't Live a Day without You" (Avalon) and "Fountain of Grace" (Twila Paris). I remember reading R. C. Sproul's book on election and reformed faith and almost hearing You speak to me: "Yes, Anne, I choose you before the beginning of time." And falling on my knees in praise and adoration.

I remember re-dedicating myself to You in late 1990s— ready to retire and serve you, and not me!

I remember one day a couple years ago, studying and not learning, and asking for Your help—and You told me: "Anne, until you are obedient to Me in respecting John, nothing else you do for Me counts for anything."

And the latest, as I am leading a study of James, and learning about trials: Count it all joy... And I learned that You did a work in me, and now, I can count it all joy!

Praise to You, My Father!

03.03.07   Again chose to write a prayer for Renovaré:

Heavenly Father, I have been thinking of this assignment all week, unsure how to begin. I'll begin with praising You—for Who You are, for what You have created, for Your love for Your children. Thank you for awakening my soul to Your glory and majesty, and Your sovereignty. Forgive me for my self-focus all my life—for filling my life with temporal things and pleasures - for focusing on me and not on You.

Thank you for Sally and the impact her faith has made on my own faith. I think I began a renewal about the time I starting working (for NCC) at home, realizing how empty and useless my goals and activities had been, and how my heart was with You, and in my home. Thank You for giving me a hunger for Christian history and world history, bringing me to a Biblical world view— for R. C. Sproul bringing me to an understanding of election.

Realizing that You had planned me, elected me, loved me, since the beginning of time. Something I think I knew in my spirit as I yearned for You, yet sought satisfaction in worldly pursuits— and did not find peace.

My personal study of reformed doctrine has answered so many questions and longings and I praise You for those writers and teachers who have persevered over two centuries, in spite of opposition and persecution.

Father, I want my life to be Yours. I dedicate my leading and teaching Bible studies to You, and I pray for guidance and wisdom. I dedicate my motherhood and grandmotherhood to You, and I pray for guidance and wisdom. I dedicate my home and my homemaker role to You, and I pray for guidance and wisdom. I especially dedicate my role as John's wife to You, and I pray for guidance and wisdom and practice of the fruit of the Spirit: love, joy, patience, kindness, gentleness, faithfulness, self-control. I pray that my friendships will honor and glorify You. Every thought, every word, every act—all to Your glory.

I pray for an awareness of my responsibility as a believer, to share the gospel, to have more concern for the lost, to be aware of opportunities to serve You in serving the poor and downtrodden. I pray for Your blessings on our family—for love for each other, patience for our mothers, spiritual growth for us all. Thank you from the depths of my soul, from the bottom of my heart, for our three precious grandchildren. How blessed we are with both daughters and their husbands.

All of these requests in Jesus' name, Amen.

05.03.07   After coming home from a trip to Columbus, I was convicted of my negative attitude toward John. I think because sometimes he seems fine, I get frustrated when his dementia takes over. I get impatient when he cannot comprehend my conversation. I pray for forgiveness and for more love and patience. John had another episode last night at midnight. He got out of bed and began sliding on his butt across the floor, using his hands as levers to propel himself out into the hallway. When I asked him what he was doing, he said he was asked to come and was trying to get up the stairs. I reminded him there was no upstairs and to come back. He slid back into the bedroom; I had to tell him to stand up. He did and went into our bathroom; was in there awhile with light on. I got up and went in there and he was fully dressed and appeared to be awake I asked him where was he going, at midnight. He said "Mother and Daddy called, and want me to come, so I am going." I reminded him it was midnight and I went back to bed, but kept my eyes open. Several times he came into the bedroom and looked at me, then went back to his closet and turned the light off, than back on. Finally he undressed and got back in bed. Next morning: no memory of any of it. An article on Lewy Body dementia in Sunday paper—scary, sad... I wonder what will happen. I foresee my staying home all the time when he gets worse.

05.14.07   Two more minor episodes last night: John "awakened" and was trying to "get a chicken out of the bed," brushing between us with his hand. I told him there was no chicken. He strongly disagreed with me, and fell asleep again. Later, he raised up in bed, brushing at the windows, to get the "silk pockets", "screens", down. No memory of either upon awakening this morning. Needless to say, I did not get much sleep.

Mother has now been here since I brought her Friday afternoon. Saturday was the worse day because she kept repeating herself over and over, and asking the same questions over and over, and I was trying to reason with her—big mistake. You can't reason with her. I decided not to try to reason with her, nor remind her that she has said that, or asked that, over and over already. I will just answer her over and over, practicing patience. If I remember that her brain is not functioning normally, I can be patient. She stands and watches me as I cook, or clean, or work, and it is unnerving, but I just try to ignore her.

05.16.07   I was so glad when Cheri came for lunch Tuesday and took Mother back with her. Joyce (sister) called and we commiserated together about Mother's loss of brain. It is so sad to not want to be around her, after loving her so much for so long. Her "religion" seems so saccharine and self-focused and smarmy. I tried to practice my Renovaré discipline while she was here—five to ten minutes of silent worship—but was unable to get my mind clear. That is difficult! This morning, John and I ate breakfast on the porch, after helping Susan with the horses. We read our scripture for the day, and prayed together. Such a blessing!

06.20.07   *I Need Thee Every Hour* comes to my mind as I begin to gather my thoughts to write about yesterday's visit to neurologist. Absolutely diagnosed now as Lewy Body dementia— no longer "mild cognitive impairment." First time John has truly accepted it. No more driving for him; he got sick and threw up on the way home. That was quite a blow to him. I assured him that I will drive him to wherever he needs to go. May give us more quality time together than we've ever had! He liked that. Unsure what

to do about week of VBS: he plans to work in VBS, but Sally and kids
will be here that week, and I don't know how to get him there and
home again.

06.23.07   John has been working on getting his truck cleaned
up to sell; this has to be hard for him. He is accepting the situation;
prays that God will be glorified in it. We have two binders of information on Lewy Body that Nancy had put together on LBD when
Reid had this—scary. We had a good day, gardening, cleaning truck,
etc. Roger had breakfast with us. He offered to drive John wherever, watch out for him while I am gone next week on NH hiking trip
with Betty. Sally has called every day to see how we are doing—told
me that Chip prayed thanks about the example we are setting in
handling this. Thank you, Lord! Sometimes when I look out into
the future I get scared; I need to take one day at a time. We both
want to honor and glorify God in how we deal with this. Nancy was
so kind and patient with Reid; I want to be that kind and patient!

07.08.07   Renovaré assignment was to take an inventory
of how I spend my life, and how well I bring God into each activity. Very timely, since John and I are praying about our activities,
which ones to continue doing, which to eliminate, etc. in light of
his not driving. I agreed to keep my responsibilities at church:
clerk, substitute Sunday school teacher, Precept leader, Women's
welcoming committee leader. John will stay with Awana (he offered to step down from his director role) and ushering, and wants

to stay on with Master Gardener for another year, when his role as treasurer expires. I am not sure what I'll do with my Free Clinic board chairmanship. We have two workshops this week; maybe I'll get an answer from God. I have another year in this three-year term. John seems to want me near him more than usual. He reads material on dementia and it bothers him. We both keep turning it all over to the Lord, but it is disconcerting. He needs to be told things over and over; continues to ask same questions; has hard time focusing on and understanding simple things. Other times (half of the time?) he seems just fine. He decided last week not to do VBS—what a relief! Too much inconvenience for too many people. Now we can enjoy Sally and kids better.

07.16.07   Sally and the kids got here Friday night; it is so nice to have them here! I know they miss the fun of the lake, but it is great to be able to enjoy them with Susan and Roger, too. Betty came for a cookout and seemed to enjoy it, and appreciated being asked. Sunday night brought a disappointment. Since last doctor appointment, John has been on medication to help him sleep and had not had any night episodes. Last night, Sally and I were still in living room; he had been in bed for about an hour. We heard a cry of anguish and a jerking on the door, and went to see what was going on. He was fighting to open the bedroom door (the wrong way). Sally's finger got smashed. When we got the door open, he was extremely agitated and sweaty and talking about using clippers. Went into bathroom to change sweaty tee shirt at my suggestion and began moving things around—"to go to bed" in the tub! No memory of this in the morning.

Too many decisions

07.29.07   Renovaré tomorrow—my assignment was to write a confession of sin in my life. My mind feels like it is spinning; I can't get my thoughts organized. It's as if I have too much to do, but when I make a list, I can get things done in a timely manner. I think I am living in the future, i.e., thinking about what our lives will be like as we move into this dementia issue. I get impatient so quickly and then I feel guilty. I almost wish all I had to do was take care of the house and John. But I'm not sure that is healthy; I probably need to have outside interests—But do I have too many? Should I cut something out? Bible study teaching, church clerk, Sunday school teaching sub, welcoming committee leader, Free Clinic board... gardening, sewing, reading all fall by the wayside.

Am I feeding my ego with these activities, or am I serving God? Is self-interest the sin I need to confess? Father, help me work through this...

08.13.07   Lots can happen in two weeks! Had a meeting Mon. July 30th with executive committee of FCFC board. I asked Dale (vice chairman) to take position of chairman and I would take over Fund Raising committee leadership. He agreed. Had 5 at meeting, all agreeable, good meeting. Now do I ever have work ahead! I did get a good group on this committee, two new members. Need God's wisdom for this! John has been doing pretty well; had a couple of minor episodes at night.

08.21.07   Had an appointment with neurologist this morning; John did well on "tests"—do not have to go back for a year! I need to be more patient as he forgets things and has difficulty with carrying on conversations. Swartzes were over for dinner last night. John and Gary were conversing a lot and it was an enjoyable evening. Grace is not as upbeat as usual—getting discouraged at lack of progress health-related. I have been trying to read Psalms and meditate—easier said than done! Psalm 42 spoke to me: Why are you downcast, O my soul—I feel almost sick most mornings, stomach upset, shoulder and elbow really hurt, slight headache, and *tired* too often. Sometimes I feel like I am "on hold" about John's condition. Waiting... wondering...

08.22.07   Every time I have sat down to meditate on Psalms, my mind has wandered and I have not stuck with it. Today, John and I are fasting for Awana—maybe that discipline will enable my mind to settle down. I am full of thoughts about preparation for our beach vacation next week, Free Clinic responsibilities, condition of our world, and especially USA... and praying for rain! Reading Psalm 89: Praise the Lord, His love, His faithfulness, His covenant.

09.03.07   We had a wonderful time at the beach with the Ewans! Our fifteenth time: Nigel was just a baby and now is almost 16. How fast time goes. We did get some rain while we were gone, and again Friday night—Praise God. John and I are reading Jeremiah these days; God's punishment on Israel and Judah is what we in the USA deserve. We pray for mercy for our deliberate lack of godliness, and for wisdom that the Holy Spirit would convict the hearts of our leaders. What is to become of us?! I am excited about starting the study of Daniel, then on to Revelation.

I am reading Spiritual Disciplines by Donald Whitney and am so convicted about how much I need to practice these disciplines, seriously and fervently. My goal is to speak and act at home as if Jesus were right here with us, which of course, He is! My sin of impatience is ever before me. For the next 15–20 minutes I will practice solitude, sitting here on the porch, enjoying the view, waiting for Brenda to call...

09.16.07   Happy 42nd birthday to Sally! What joy she has given us, and I am sure, God. Today started out terrible. I lost my temper with John before we left for church; stayed angry too long and made myself sick with remorse. Self-denial?! I fail miserably, Lord—help me! A beautiful day, rather cool, but so nice after weeks of hot weather. I have sat outside on the porch, working on Precepts in Daniel 1-6. Listening to Pachelbel's Canon now; preparing to read more about spiritual disciplines. How I need them!

09.23.07   What a week! I have talked more to my sisters this week than in the past year! What to do with Mother?! She has no memory at all, except to dress, eat, and go to church. We have agreed she needs to go to a retirement/nursing home. Went to an Extraordinary Women conference in Lynchburg Fri through Sat with Joyce. Enjoyed so much being with her! Another "laughable" event in the Lewy Body experience: Sometimes I snore and John goes into another bedroom. This morning I was awakened at 5:45 by the radio alarm clock. Got up, dressed, made the bed, went into the kitchen to make coffee, looked at the clock in the kitchen: it was 4:39 AM! I was wide awake by then, so stayed up and worked on church clerk duties, and read commentary on Daniel. As I was praying, I felt God was telling me to bring Mother to live with me until we decide where she should be. Eek! eek! But I am willing to take her in if that is what God wants me to do. I just need to ensure that John is OK with it. Note: John had set the alarm, but in doing

so, had inadvertently reset the time on it! Praise God I did not get
upset, but appreciated the extra hours in the day!

09.24.07   My 65th birthday! I got up at 6:45 AM, still studying Daniel! Just sent an email note of encouragement to the students; this is difficult to understand! Spent about an hour on the
phone, with Cheri, with Richfield Assisted Living, and with Nancy.
I offered to let Mother stay here until we can get her into Richfield.
Cheri and I are meeting at Richfield on Wednesday to discuss
financial arrangements, etc. Weeded around the horse arena in the
afternoon; went to Grace and Gary's for dinner; she invited Susan
and Roger, too, for Susan's 40th birthday! This is the fifth year we
have celebrated birthdays together!

09.28.07   Cheri and I visited Richfield this morning and were
pleasantly surprised. It is very nice; now to convince Mother. She
had told Nancy she would not be happy moving unless it was into a
house. Joyce is coming next Thursday and I will go pick up Mother
and bring her here while they handle the move. I have thought a lot
about just letting her live with us, but I keep remembering how she
stays underfoot and is so annoying with repetition and inane comments for which she expects responses. With John's situation, too,
I am not sure how I could handle both. John and I were working in
the the yard this afternoon and he just does not seem to be able to
think for himself Can he not? or am I so critical and he was being
cautious? Most of the time he seems OK, but he does not get into

projects right away like he always had. He watches TV almost all
the time he is in the house. Oh well, he is sweet and loving...

10.07.07   This has been a most trying weekend, and I am failing the tests. Mother is so annoying and it is not her fault. I drove
to her house Friday to pick her up and bring her here for the weekend. By dinner Friday night, she had asked me seven times when
would she go to "that retirement home," and how far was it from
me, and many other questions related to the move. I lost patience
with her, and then apologized, but she is relentless in her repetition and questioning. She cannot remember from five minutes to
the next; does not even remember that she asks questions over and
over. At church I kept wondering if God wants me to offer her a
home with us, but on the way home, she started in again. It is like
she won't believe us or wants us to change plans. I hate not to want
her around, but she drives us crazy. If she couldn't (or wouldn't)
talk, it would be ok! I will be so glad to take her to Cheri's tomorrow. I think we will all like her better after Tuesday when she gets
into Richfield. An hour at a time is better than days at a time! Since
I am failing this test of patience, I am sure more "chances" will
come, with John's condition! I am reading John Piper's *The Root of
Endurance* sitting on the porch on a beautiful Sunday afternoon. I
have prayed often about my busy schedule, and what to eliminate.
As I read about Wilberforce and his care for the poor, I think I will
not give up my role in the Free Clinic. I have pondered my motives
for my role on the board: prestige? serving the poor? enjoying the

fellowship? I do believe free clinics are doing Christ's work, and it is an opportunity to serve Him, especially in an area where my life and faith could influence non-believers. My second term goes for another year; I'll hang in there!

Being a caregiver

10.22.07   John forgot to take his med Saturday night, so "woke up" a couple of times with episodes. I did not get much rest and was really sleepy Sunday! After church, we went to Richfield to see Mother, but she was at chapel, so we went by and visited with Nancy a few minutes before coming to Massanutten for a week. Got into our condo around 4 PM, and crashed. Rested well. We had a great day today. It was a beautiful day: lots of color with fall leaves. Went to water aerobics in the morning, played tennis awhile, then hiked for several hours after lunch.

10.23.07   Our beloved Nigel's 16th birthday! What a joy he has been! John and I had another nice day here at Massanutten.

10.24.07   I called Nigel this morning; how I love that boy! and Parker and Dempsey! We are so blessed. A rainy day; can't complain since we need it so badly and have prayed so much for the rain. We did water aerobics, went shopping to fill a shoe box for Samaritan's Purse. Went for a walk alone late afternoon; now settled down for a quiet evening. I did call Joyce to wish her a happy birthday. John has become so attached, and follows me around, watching what I do. Maybe to see where he can be of help? I wish I could be less impatient.

11.02.07   Great time with Ewans, as always. Continuing to pray that Nancy's NC house sells, and for more rain. I have missed Renovaré for 3 weeks. Need to catch up and practice, especially contemplation. I have felt less anxious lately, although FCFC fund raising is still weighing heavily on my mind. I pray God will give me joy in that task.

11.10.07   Busy, busy, busy.... Went out Tuesday, to vote, met Louise for breakfast, visited Mother at Richfield, to ophthalmologist for John's eye "floaters," to Nancy's to meet her and Cheri for lunch. By the time we got back home, around 4 PM, John was so confused. Too much in one day!

11.13.07   Praise God for a calm spirit! I am still working on being more calm and patient, but am so thankful for the time at home this week, and last week. I just get harried when I have to go out every day!

Praying for 2008's US president—a godly man, please, Lord! Prayer for next pastor. prayer for John, to be at peace and not worry about his dementia—for healing? Your will be done.

11.20.07   A teary time this morning in our prayer time: John is not "getting" what I say very often, looks confused when I am saying something and when he responds, it is not logical. I get impatient, forgive me, Lord. I pray for patience, kindness, love, tenderness to him. We both know this is of You, and that Your plans are right and fair. Help us to live like we believe it! Give me wisdom in what I do with my time, and what John and I should continue to do. I read Francis Schaeffer's *A Christian Manifesto*—wow, powerful! and convicting! Two world views, totally incompatible. Christ does not fit in a box; He is Lord of *all*. Humanism is a religion, a faith in man, but reduces Man to less than God made him. Penn: "If we are not ruled by God, then we are ruled by tyrants." Destruction of faith and freedom leads to no absolutes; personal choice is king. God, help us know what we should do!

11.23.07   John got out of the house at midnight Wednesday night. I woke up and saw him trying to open the door from our bedroom onto the porch. He finally did, went out, tried to get back in through the door to the kitchen. Came back to bedroom door and

came in; he was out about 5 minutes. Got back in bed, and said to
me, "I'll leave as soon as I can," and went to sleep. Didn't remember any of it next morning. Guess I won't be leaving him alone at
night anymore. Susan said he can stay with them if necessary. He
had minor episodes on the 17th and 18th—maybe needs stronger
dosage, to sleep better? Thanksgiving here was nice; Mother,
Louise, Nancy, Cheri and Rafael, then Susan and Roger, and his
parents for dessert with us. Mother did not know Louise. Louise
had another car accident Friday; her fault. Had to go to hospital for
x-rays. Decisions to be made now; praying for wisdom and guidance.

11.27.07   Had a meeting in Roanoke to follow up on FCFC
workshops we had in August. After the meeting, I handed in my
resignation, with tears. But a load off my back. Sunday afternoon
was another really bad scene. John broke a lamp and I fell apart.
No excuses, but capped my decision to reduce my activities. He is
getting worse and I need my energy for dealing with him. So many
friends have offered to help, but nothing they can do yet, other
than sit with him, and let me get out. Later perhaps. He and I went
for a long walk this morning—nice. I did not feel rushed. Sally and
the kids are on their way to see us.

12.04.07   Great visit with Sally and wonderful kids. Thank
you, Lord, for them! House is now decorated for Christmas. John's
night time meds are not working well lately. He has been having

episodes again. Last night he got up and walked around the house at 10:30 PM. Then at midnight, he got up again, and tried to get outside through bedroom door to porch. Couldn't unlock it. Went in to bathroom and I assumed he was awake. He got dressed and tried again to get outside. Then undressed and got back in bed. Did not remember any of it next morning.

Louise is calling several times a day. We are checking out Richfield to get her in an apt. there.

12.07.07   Had five minutes of solitude: the joy of the Lord is my strength! As I began my period of silence, I gave my heart over to my beloved Renovaré friends, not in words, but in love, to God for them, and their requests of Him. Joyous! My heart is light and my joy is full—how different from a couple weeks ago when I felt so down and stressed out. Thank you, Heavenly Father!

12.09.07   No five minutes yesterday! I tried several times. At least John and I have our own devotional time together every morning. His reading ability has decreased and I was getting so edgy and not worshipping as he read. God has helped me to be patient, and just thankful John wants to read the Bible and pray. We went to a Sunday School Class party last night; he seemed to enjoy it, but got irritable when ready to go. He has slept in front of TV off and on all afternoon. Went to Susan and Roger's for dinner this evening; they notice his decline in speech and logical thinking. We

read 1 Tim. today; convicted me on part about widows. Maybe we
are expecting too much from Louise's church. We need to take the
responsibility to help her!

12.10.07   I wish I were able to capture the epiphany I experienced this morning while baking cookies. I was enjoying myself
and feeling good, thinking of God's goodness. Also thinking of
John's condition and it then occurred to me how many friends
have commented on our having this burden. It was as if God said to
me: "This is how I want you to serve Me and honor Me." I thought
about something I read some time ago: that God gives His children
trials to bring honor to Himself. I realized we are blessed to have
this opportunity. Now to live as if we know this is an honor! This
may be what He had prepared for us to do for His glory. (Eph. 2:10)

"It is well with my soul."

12.12.07   Another spell last night around ˆ9 AM. He got
up and was trying to pull my pillow out from under my heard
and pulling sheet and blanket off the bed. Making unintelligible
sounds, almost angry. Went into bathroom , turned on light, peed,
got dressed, walked around in bedroom, got undressed and into
bed. Looked at me, looking at him, and said "Hi." I asked if he
meant to leave the light on; he got up and turned it off, got back
into bed, and went to sleep. No memory of any of it next morning. I
had been afraid he would have an episode, for two reasons: he had

struggled for two or more hours in the evening with the Master Gardener bank statements and records. I helped him with that; he had not balanced the check book since March. Got that up to date, but could tell it really confused him. Then he forgot his "sleeping pill" and had to get up after going to bed at 10, to take it. He needs to take it an hour before bedtime. (I need to start doing the pills for him!)

12.21.07   Two more spells this week—same as usual. Wed. and Thur. nights he slept in guest bedroom because he has a terrible cold. I got two good nights sleep! Went to GP on Monday and asked him if he could handle prescriptions for John, since his neurologist has left the practice. Asked about and got script for Namenda, along with Aricept. Saw article in paper about playing cards being good for mind. Got out cards to play double solitaire. He could not even lay the cards out right, much less play—like teaching little child to play. Doctor told him *not* to use power tools any more. We are doing some workshop clean up this week. Organizing them for future selling/giving away. how sad. What next?

12.29.07   Wonderful Christmas with Ewans! Had a nice dinner and evening with Susan and Roger before we left for Ohio. We gave everyone money this year; getting more difficult to know what to buy for presents. Bought coat for Dempsey; made fake fur muff and hat for her. Susan and Roger had Louise to their house for Christmas - Bless them! Got our house back to normal yesterday;

did not sleep well, so tired today. Bad cold. Rained a lot yesterday—
praise God! Today is cloudy and dreary—suits my having a cold
and taking it easy! Wondering what this time next year will bring...
how John will be doing... if Louise or Mother will be here or
in heaven.

Reading more on End Times, to fit in with the Daniel study and
upcoming study of Revelation. John and I read Bible through
this year—too fast! I kept wanting to stop and research and study
more deeply. Chip kidded us about moving near them; if Susan and
Roger were not here, it would be tempting. Looking back, I wonder
if we made the right move in 2000. But I wanted to get away from
where I was so self-absorbed and "start over" spiritually. Also,
Louise has needed us. It is nice to live close to Susan and Roger,
Cheri, Nancy and Betty!

Reading Schaeffer's *True Spirituality* now. Wondering why we
never learn about "dying to self" when we are young—not listening? It is so clear to me that I have spent most of my life focused on
me, in the world's culture, not seeing that the world is not my home.
Yet knowing that deep in my soul, but not willing to give up my
quest for personal honor and accolades. Thank God I finally know
that my happiness and satisfaction can only come from a right
relationship with Him.

12.31.07   Only a few hours left in 2007. What a year! I sup-
pose the major events for us are: our first year in this house; adjust-
ing to being close "neighbors" of daughter and son-in-law; John's
progression with dementia and his having to give up driving;
Mother in Richfield Assisted Living; Nancy moving to Salem; Louise's car wreck and her no longer driving; my resigning from Free
Clinic board. I still have mixed emotions from the latter; I think if
I had stayed on as chairman rather than fund-raising committee
chair, I might have stayed on. But the pressures of fund-raising
were overwhelming me at a time when John's situation and Mother's move got to me. I will miss that group! Our annual New Year's
Eve day dinner with the Swartzes and Whitleys was cancelled this
morning; Grace is not doing well. We all are concerned about the
cancer causing her recent physical problems. I was not sorry to be
able to be at home today, but I was sorry not to be able to end this
year and start the new year like we have done for 5 years now.

9:30 PM: Susan and Roger here for dinner; then we played Chronology for awhile. John did ok, although it was apparent that his
logic skills are weak. Brenda called for our regular prayer time;
I had neglected to let her know Susan and Roger would be here.
Then Grace called; was feeling somewhat better, but not good. Not
much in this journal about Precept lessons or students. Odd, since
this is such a major part of my life. My whole calendar revolves
around Thursday mornings! I love the studies, the discipline, and
especially the women who attend. Neither did I say much about

Larry and Ginger, and how much they mean to us. We have been in many churches in our married life, moving from place to place. We have felt more a part of this church than any of the others; Larry is a wonderful, humble, kind, loving, Spirit-filled man. He is ready to retire and we hate to see him leave. He will mentor the new pastor for awhile. We drive by five other Baptist churches on our way in to FHBC, but how we love our "family" there! It would be hard to leave them!

Another new year

01.04.08   A new year—what will it bring? My (our) prayer
is that God will be honored in our lives. Our new year was not
started off as it had been for the past five years, with the Swartzes
and Whitleys. Bob died end of 2006, and I wonder if we will have
Grace with us by the end of this year. This will be our second year
with John's dementia, although I do wonder how long he has had
it; I remember odd behaviors for a number of years. Here is where
he stands now: still having "night episodes," usually between
midnight and 1 AM. These had stopped for awhile when he started
a medicine to help him have a deeper sleep, but started up again
lately, not as frequently, nor as severe. He began taking Namenda,
along with Aricept, before Christmas. The only difference I see

is that he is reading better; his reading (Bible aloud daily with me) had become really bad. He continues to have trouble grasping ideas and instructions. Some things he can handle well; some things he just doesn't "get." We tried solitaire and he was lost, but he played checkers with Parker and was fine. Could answer questions playing Chronology, but couldn't figure out where cards should be placed. He has given up treasurer of Master Gardener, but will stay a member. I will miss Free Clinic board, but am relieved not to have that responsibility. He and I are walking daily and spending more time together. With Louise now unable to drive, we will be doing things for her.

01.05.08   Nancy's house has not sold, and the expenses for Mother at Richfield are steep; we are considering moving her to an apartment. Betty and I took a nice hike at Fairystone State Park today—WOW—praises to God for beautiful creation! Even in January! Betty gave me a news clipping about Alzheimer's and caregivers. One out of three caregivers die before their loved one—stress. John read it and noted that comment. I do wish he had friends to enjoy time with, so I would be more comfortable going off with my friends. Reading Walvoord's *Armageddon, Oil, and Terror* now: even so, come Lord Jesus!

01.08.08   Pastor's sermon on knowing God's will: can't know it unless we are being obedient. "Honor thy father and mother"— are we obedient, Lord? Mother's mantra: "with four daughters,

why won't one of them let me live with her?" I emailed my sisters,
my daughters, and my Renovaré group with a plan to bring both
Louise and Mother here to live in an "apartment" we could fix up
in our basement, asking for their prayers and thoughts.

Resoundingly no, not a good idea, for a number of reasons, not the
least of which is John's situation. John and I walked the trail at
Fairystone Park Monday morning, enjoyed it, and plan to continue
walking/hiking daily. He expressed depressed feelings Sunday and
Monday—unsure how to help him. I will show him more love and
kindness...

01.15.08   Experienced God's presence several times this
week; praises to His Name! Hiked at Fairystone again Sat., with
Betty. His creation is awesome! Saw several beautiful sunsets and
sun rises! God gave me help/wisdom to lead study at nursing home,
on *joy,* a fruit of the Spirit. What a blessing for me, hopefully for
them! Began teaching Genesis to Audrey's Sunday School class
while she is in Florida. Still wondering if I should bring Mother
here to live? or Louise? Trinity nursing home is so sad, don't want
them there. The past week has made me aware that with God's
help, I am able to produce fruit of the Spirit. My goal (in Renovaré)
was to choose someone (John) to exercise any of the fruits on:
love, patience, kindness. I did and it was wonderful! God did all
the "fruit" in me. I realized on Saturday that I had not really given
much thought to my goal, but had been more kind, loving, patient

and self-controlled through Him! 4 PM: How wonderful to be with
all 4 of my Renovaré friends today; how I love them! Thanks be to
God for friends who love Him and serve Him so faithfully.

01.22.08   Called Cheri to wish her a Happy Birthday; I love
my sisters so much! John's birthday was quiet. Had "tea" with
Susan and Roger on Sunday afternoon; nice reminder of our trip to
Great Britain!

02.04.08   Renovaré "assignment": help a friend in need. Took
Louise to doctor and grocery; blessed for doing this. Went to see
Betty for awhile afterwards; we had planned a trip to hike in North
Carolina in May. Should I leave John or not? Decided last night not
to go; I need You, Father, to have joy in unselfishness.

02.05.08   Praises to God! Oh the joy that comes from obedience to Your Word! Weight lifted about hiking trip decision; thank
God for understanding friends like Betty! I pray she will go anyway
and have fun.

02.05.08   A good week! Thank you, Lord, for continuing to
live through me with the fruit of the Spirit. I talked to Mother on
Tuesday; she seems to go in and out mentally. Confused me with
Nancy. John's cell phone is broken, so we went to get it repaired
or replaced. Got him a new one, especially for older people. I was
trying to help him record a message, and he got agitated; could not

do it. Finally agreed he doesn't need one, so I'll return it. He and I worked clearing vines from woods Friday and Saturday—enjoyed it! Today we have winds 40–60mph; electricity went out. Thank God we had the generator installed last year! Read chapter on fasting several times from Spiritual Disciplines by Whitney. I hope to fast tomorrow; for humility before God. Met new pastor Stan and wife Susan; very personable. We will miss Larry and Ginger; I am so glad they plan to stay as part of the church family.

02.11.08   Fasted from last night supper to tonight's supper; had juice, coffee and water. Thought of God so often; felt so close to Him. John told me while he was eating his lunch that he would fast with me next time I want to fast. My reason this time was to worship God. The book I am studying names ten categories of purposes for fasting. I was convicted reading that Jesus *expects* us to fast, i.e, "*When* you fast..." not *if.*

02.18.08   for my Renovaré assignment: "Choose a day to do everything in honor of God..." I have thought of this every morning and yet the day goes by without another conscious thought of it. Today I will try to remind myself, perhaps by choosing to fast during the day. Have had Grace on my mind so often lately; so concerned about her health, her choice of medical treatments, and their inability to find a church that suits them.

02.22.08   Hunger, or even thinking about food, really draws us to the Lord. I had to go without food or drink Wednesday dinner thru Thursday lunch, for blood test for thyroid. This time I felt sick; maybe because I was not doing it for spiritual reasons! I may BE sick; I still feel pretty bad with headache, sore throat, etc. Went to doc. Wed. morning for a check up; seem healthy. I am glad to be home today and tomorrow; lots of housework to do. Getting John to help with some of it. I told him I feel bad asking, but if he wants to: dust, feed birds, dishwasher duty! Teaching both Sunday School and Precept is heavy study, but wonderful. I plan to wear a rubber band on my wrist to remind me that everything I do today is to honor God. I just wrote my "to-do" list, and already feel better— seeing it on paper helps me see it is not more than I can handle!

Busy day Wed! John to Louise's, me to tax guy, then to Betty's, doctor appointments, John's Master Gardener meeting, met Homer and Nella for dinner. Homer has prostate cancer; will have 40 radiation treatments! Almost finished with Daniel study; will start Revelation study in March. What a blessing Daniel study has been! Thank you, God! Enjoyed last Tuesday evening with Susan, Nancy and Cheri.

Vacation!

03.03.08   To quote the TV ad: "Life comes at you fast!" John
and I are at Lake Lure, North Carolina this week at Fairfield
Mountains resort, using a week of Susan and Roger's timeshare
they couldn't use. A beautiful day—more like May than March!

We signed up for a timeshare, against my better judgement, but
John wanted to do it. He is getting worse and really likes the two of
us getting away together.

John is no longer able to use a credit card when pumping gas; gets
confused. Has hard time figuring 15% tips (don't we all!); conversation is difficult: he uses incorrect words and too few words, i.e.,

ten words when 100 are needed. Often talks on and on with no

point. How nice it is to be sitting outside on the deck today; we ate

lunch out here—first time this year! Now I am studying for Sunday

School: Genesis 29–31; Thank You, Father, for this opportunity to

teach Genesis; I study much more than if I were just sitting

in a class.

03.04.08   I must not be leaning on the Lord well these days. I

have had two blow-ups—today's was scary. I thought I was losing

my mind. John had fallen while hitting the tennis ball, and hurt

his ankle. We were going to the hospital near the resort, and I was

expecting John to be helping me find the hospital. The map was

clearly marked, but we had to turn around several times, stopped

and asked directions several times... My nerves were shot; I was

trying not to feel resentment that he had to go to emergency room.

As it turned out, x-rays did not show any damage, but he may have

sprained it. If not better in one week, we go to an orthopedic doc-

tor. I was in terrible emotional shape, shaking and just wanting to

scream. I kept praying for help from God; I knew this was a sinful

reaction. Finally after more than two hours, and intermittent

reading commentary on Genesis, I knew God was with me. Sally

was praying, even during the worst part of my "emotional break-

down" (it felt like that!). I told John I will not expect him to be my

navigator again; I should not have expected him to be. Thank you,

God, for loving me, through such a horrid time, and please, Lord,

let me *never* "go there" again.

03.06.08 Praise God for a nice day yesterday—a beautiful day and an enjoyable day! We went into the town of Lake Lure—bought a red sun hat and a small braided rug for Susan. Had a nice lunch overlooking the lake. I took a good walk for about an hour—just around the resort. Another sunny day today. Had a good night's sleep, first in awhile. Read Joshua again, and prayed together. Not sure whether to go back for the Women's Conference this weekend, or stay here until Saturday. I'll let John decide. He seemed a little restless yesterday afternoon, unable to do much. He should keep off his feet.

03.07.08 What a beautiful, enjoyable day! If it would continue, I think we would stay until Saturday, but it turns cooler and rainy tomorrow. We played miniature golf before lunch; had a nice lunch at the club house; went kayaking for a couple of hours in the afternoon. Nice! I do wish I were more understanding of John's inability to comprehend and converse. Maybe some day I will get there. I try to chat, and he doesn't seem to comprehend what I am saying, so if and when he responds, it usually doesn't make sense. Then I get impatient and/or irritable. God help me...

03.08.08 Home again! Drove home yesterday morning in pouring rain. Had a word from God as I was driving along, thinking and praying. The scripture where Jesus said: "In as much as you have done it to the least of these My brethren, you have done it unto Me, " came to my mind.... I believe God was telling me that how I treat John and respond to him is counted as the way I respond to God Himself.

03.10.08   It is amazing how often that verse comes to mind! And subsequently, how much nicer I am! Thank You, Lord! A beautiful day; John and I worked in the yard and enjoyed that!

Another world out there

03.18.08   Interesting week... Fasted 24 hours Wednesday morning to Thursday morning. John fasted until Wednesday night Awana pizza night! Learned from Brenda that NCC (my former employer) is in a heap of trouble financially. Our stock previously valued at over half a million is now worth less than half of that. Thank God we know He is in charge; He is sovereign. I've been running almost every day back and forth Roanoke - Rocky Mount - home. I need to quit something, or accept the fact that it is going to cost $40/week for gas! John and I have been working in the yard often, hoping for a *lawn*! We enjoy the work; turned the ground in my garden yesterday to prepare it. Sunday was such a blessing. Woke up feeling rather defeated, but got up and got ready for church; soon felt fine. The message was on the cross, wonderful music, contributed to a feeling of blessedness. Good Sunday School class. After lunch, I talked to Betty, then Sally, then began my Revelation study. I felt euphoric—truly loved and blessed by God! Revelation 1:3: "Blessed is he who reads this and does it!"

Obedience in my responding to John also is a contributor to this oneness with God. I am fasting from breakfast to dinner today, and praying for Grace and Gary.

03.24.08   My "assignment" this week has been to allow the Holy Sprit to become part of my prayer life. I would hope that I always do that, but I want to be conscious of it. I lay awake last night as many hours as I slept, praying for so many concerns. So many specific prayer requests don't ever seem to be answered. I can only trust that God is working in these situations. We had a nice Easter: wonderful worship service. dinner here with family and friends. Praying about summer Bible study; after several months of teaching both Precepts and Sunday school, I am ready for a break. But want to obey God's leading. Oh God, I want/need to learn how to work with John's dementia! Another screaming fit this morning, as I was trying to enter his Master Gardener hours into a computer program. Asking yes or no questions and getting long answers making no sense. After trying for several minutes, and getting nowhere;
I lost patience.

03.29.08   Feeling rather addled this morning... need Holy
Spirit to pray *for* me. I offered to take over Mother's finances since
Nancy is moving back to North Carolina. Talked to Louise this
morning to let her know we will come and take care of her needs
on Monday (grocery shopping and finances)—talking to her always
leaves me addled! She jumps around so. Gary coming for dinner tonight, along with Roger. Grace is in a treatment center, and Susan
is at a horse event. Need to clean house and cook! Are any of these
things less important than teaching Bible? Mary? Martha?

03.31.08   Invited Gary to dinner again, and offered to do yard
work for Grace's gardens. Kept nursery at church. Taking Louise
shopping Wednesday. Felt kinda overwhelmed last week, trying to
keep up with managing our household, Louise's finances, Precept,
Sunday school lesson to prepare, etc. etc. If my gift if teaching, I
should teach. But the other responsibilities are important, too,
and I can honor God with my attitude as I do these things. Thanks
be to God for much needed rain! Praise God! Nancy said she will
continue to keep Mother's finances. Sunday School teacher is back
and ready to take her class again. I will miss teaching those super
ladies, but glad to be back to preparing only one lesson a week!

04.05.08   Waking up with heavy feeling; got OK as morning
progresses. Anxiety? over John? over Nancy's financial situation?
over my own sinfulness and lack of humility? Had plans to go
clean up Grace's gardens, but it rained. I helped Susan with clean

up in her azaleas and with the horses instead. Went to Louise's
Wednesday; took her grocery shopping and out to dinner. Her
constant chattering is a real test of patience!

I met Betty and her two sisters-in-law after Precepts Thursday.
Nice lunch and visit. Then they came here yesterday for tea. Enjoyable time. Jittery today; uneasy, headachy. Wonder if it is the
continued cloudy days / missing Sally and family. Heavenly Father,
let me experience the joy of *you*!

04.07.08   Realized Saturday that I am anxious, which is a
sin. read Scripture admonishing not to be anxious, and repented.
Much better Sunday! Said goodbye to Sunday School class; I'll miss
them. Rainy day today: hope to get a lot done inside. Spent several
hours on Precept lesson.

04.21.08   Went to see Grace last Thursday; wouldn't have
recognized her on the street. Amazing how losing that much
weight can change even facial features; but she is still pretty! *Very*
weak; doubt if she will be with us much longer. Brenda has been
keeping me posted on the fate of National City. My half-million
investment has decreased by 80%! Investors have come in and now
own 50%; hope things improve. So sorry for shareholders dependent on it, and for those unaware of God's ownership of everything.
Praising God for much-needed rain! Had to get Rick (our builder)
out to clean our gutters and fix them so birds cannot try to build

nests again! Buckets of twigs and sticks from the gutters! Brenda
and I continue to study Spiritual Disciplines—on prayer now. I am
focusing on reading Scripture, then meditating on it, then praying.
Renovaré group is coming here for lunch and meeting tomorrow.
We plan to review the disciplines again: Contemplative, Holiness,
Spiritual, Social justice, Evangelical, Incarnational.

04.22.08   Am I using my time wisely? Since not teaching
Sunday school, I have more time to read for pleasure. I have read
four novels in the past two weeks, entertaining, but not edifying.
Back now to *History of the Jews* by Paul Johnson. I am learning to
be joyful in serving others and less self-focused. Ephesians 2:10 is
where I want to be.

"How is John?" is a question I get frequently. His reading Scripture
every morning is an indicator: getting more stumbling lately. Conversations more non-sequitor. Also he is getting more possessive
of me—almost stifling at times. Follows me like Mother does when
she is here. I try not to show annoyance, but can tease him about it.

Nancy's lake house may sell; she is looking for another house in the
Denver, NC area; no action on house in Salem.

04.23.08   Another Precept exercise in prayer; when did I first
know God's presence:

Heavenly Father,

I cannot with certainty say the exact time was first aware of your presence. It had to have been in my childhood, since I made a profession of faith at seven years old. I am not even sure of what this means: to be aware of Your presence, i.e., to just know You are with me, or to really experience a Being. In 1993 when my Dad was dying, I experienced a real presence in the wee hours of the morning, assuring me about Dad, and that we would all be alright. No voice, just an assurance. It may have been an angel, or even Christ, there. When I understood the doctrine of election, and that You had chosen me for Your own, I knew You were there in that room. Usually, Your "presence" is more of an awareness of something You are teaching me through Your word or in prayer. For example, clarifying something as I prepare lessons or reminding me of how I need to deal with John and this illness.

Thank You, Lord, for leading me, loving me, teaching me who I am in You and who I should be in You. You are my life. Amen.

Why do I wake up with a heavy heart? A dread, a weight. Purify me, Lord, and give me joy in You. Thank You for Christian fellowship, but let me not be dependent on it, but only on You. I woke up this morning with severe pain around my heart—similar to sharp pain experienced last Thursday morning in Bible study class.

04.29.08   No more of that sharp pain, but still that waking-up depression. Anxiety? Forgive me, Lord, and help me.

> I waited patiently for the Lord; he inclined to me and heard my cry. He drew me up from the pit of destruction, out of the miry bog, and set my feet upon a rock, making my steps secure. He put a new song in my mouth, a song of praise to our God. Many will see and fear, and put their trust in the Lord.
>
> (Psalm 40:1-3)

Had wonderful visit with Ewans; Nigel was great in his roles as Benjamin and the cupbearer in "Joseph and the Amazing Technicolor Dreamcoat". Sally is always a great hostess—so solicitous of us and our comforts!

Comfort even in suffering

3 PM: Had an interesting day today. Woke up at 5 AM with the heavy heart and anxious feeling; wanted to cry, for no apparent reason. Breakfast, Bible reading and prayer with John, read newspaper, then to Susan's to help with her horse jumping. Came home still feeling anguish and weepiness, phone rang it was Kevin Snyder, the Ewan's pastor, to say he was sorry we had not had a chance to "say hello and hug" as usual. He had chatted with John and Chip, but I was not able to catch up with him. We talked awhile and he was so supportive and encouraging to me in my sadness. He prayed before we hung up. Then Betty and I talked and she told me about an email Margie had sent Saturday: Grace is dying, with only a month to go... That accounts for my spiritual malaise today. Even

though I did not know the prognosis, my spirit and our tie with God must have known. I had talked to her briefly before I saw the email, but she had not mentioned this. I plan to go see her tomorrow afternoon. Renovaré was such a comfort and a blessing. Tara has had the same deep malaise some mornings; Vickie has had same heart pain in suffering. Joyce always relates and gives comfort.

05.07.08   No morning malaise this past week—thank you, Lord. My emotional/spiritual problem is an increasing irritability with John's smothering me: touching, watching, kissing, following me around. I wish I could respond better; most times I want to just say, "Leave me alone!" (I don't) We went to the Swartzes' last Friday and yesterday, working in her flower gardens. Got to visit a little while, but you can tell she is so tired. I'll be surprised if she lives another two weeks. I will miss her so much. Precept study is over May 15; will teach Sunday School class again for a few weeks after that. John is going to have surgery on his knee May 14. Outpatient, but will have anesthesia, so will need attention for a couple of days. I had an EKG this morning, because of the chest pain. Then to Roanoke to take Louise to lunch and shopping. Had time to visit, but John was agitated (she does that to him) so we left and are now at church. This is his last Awana for the season, so we will not be coming to church Wednesday nights for awhile.

05.13.08   John and I went back to Swartzes' to work in the
gardens again. I visited with her briefly and said to myself that
may be the last time... it was. She went back in the hospital on
the 9th and died 6:20 PM on the 10th. I was in Columbus when
Janelle called to tell me. Praise to God for eternal life and no more
suffering. Sadness at losing such a good friend. I pray we stay
friends with Gary and Margie. We had a wonderful time (again) in
Cleveland; Susan I went to Columbus Thursday, then the four of
us gals went to Cleveland Friday morning. Went to Orchestra, Art
Museum, conservatory, Tower City, Morton's for dinner! Saturday
to West Side Market, Great Lakes Brewing Co. for lunch, outlet
mall and back home to Sally's. Church Sunday, and home again.
Visited Mother at Richfield—so sad...

> More than that, we rejoice in our sufferings, knowing that suf-
> fering gproduces endurance, and endurance produces char-
> acter, and character produces hope, and hope does not put us
> to shame, because God's love has been poured into our hearts
> through the Holy Spirit who has been given to us.
> (Romans 5:3-5)

"My girls" were so sweet and tender about my losing my friend
Grace. Busy week with John's surgery Wednesday. Grace's visita-
tion Thursday; last Precept class Thursday; funeral Friday. My
mind is jumbled; having a hard time focusing on studying. Want to
just stay active, but need to rest in God.

05.19.08   I miss Grace. I pray for Gary and Margie in their grief and loneliness. The funeral was nice; Gary's brother Dan gave the message and presented the gospel. Even though John had knee surgery Wednesday, he went to visit Thursday evening and funeral Friday morning. What a beautiful, comfortable friendship we shared.

05.26.08   Memorial Day. I am "good" tired—physical labor for several days. Worked in yard Saturday and today. Yesterday was "bringing in the sheaves" of hay for the horses with the Holleys and Sue and Roger. Great harvest this Spring with all the nice rains we've had—thank you, Lord! Roger's parents came Thursday through Tuesday to help with the haying. Susan was in Lexington for horse event, so we had them up here for dinner Friday and Saturday evenings. Nice folks! I have spent time relaxing on the porch almost every afternoon. Reading some mysteries. Had some quiet time, but still have trouble really settling down for more than a few minutes. I was working in the garden across the street today and did stop and sit on the bench a couple of times and talk with God.

05.28.08   John's knee seems fine. John's dementia: I marvel at how sweet he is and uncomplaining, even though he is aware of what is going on. He seemed lost at times Sunday, bringing in the hay bales. unsure of what to do. Monday night another episode— jumped up pulling sheet off the bed, went to doors as if to go out, shouted something unintelligible. I pulled on other end of sheet

and he jumped back in bed, lay with his head propped up on his
hand awhile, then slept. Tuesday night he went to the bathroom
around 1 AM, came back in bedroom but left light on. I asked him
to turn off the lights; he said there were still some people in there.
I told him no one was in there, so he turned off lights, and came
back to bed, to sleep. Mother's dementia: I called to let her know
John and I were coming to see her Wednesday morning. She called
Nancy twice asking why she was not there. She has called Nancy
ten times in one week. When John and I got there today, she was
not in her wing of building. We went to the hair salon, and there
she was, waiting to get her hair done. She smiled at us, but did not
know us. We sat down and visited with her there for awhile; she
was only focused on getting her hair done. From there, we went to
Louise's to lunch, to grocery, now we are both worn
out emotionally!

06.03.08   A good week for gardening and yard work; some
rain, but praying for more. I am reading Kingsolver's *Animal,*
Vegetable, Miracle, about producing your own food, or only buying
locally-grown food, because of the price of fuel to transport food,
and also to support local farming. Makes me want to plant more
and raise chickens! John has been having night episodes again—
several in the last week—he gets back to sleep but I don't, so I
suggested he may need to sleep in guest bedroom. He doesn't want
to, so he may start taking more meds for sleeping. I lost my temper
Friday night when he broke the lamp by the bed. I should have re-

alized it was not his fault! I feel like I am demented too! A prayer in my journal contains these words: "Allow us to be balanced, stable, and consistent Christians as Your Spirit fills us and motivates us." Amen!

06.10.08   Had a difficult week with John. He seems much worse, so quickly. Nine out of ten nights he has had those weird episodes. Cannot seem to focus on what he is doing, wants to help but cannot follow instructions/directions. Brenda suggested last night that maybe it was the surgery. I had been told that "going under" anesthesia can cause rapid decline in dementia. Had six of us here for Renovaré today: Joyce is in Olympia visiting her Renovaré group there! Suz suggested that I might not have accepted John's dementia. Some discussion followed; I agreed that I *had* accepted the diagnosis, but not the reality and the actuality of what it does. Becky suggested I try St. John's wort to help me deal with my own emotions. Thank God for this group of friends! My goal is to stop trying to "figure out" the why's of John's behavior, but to just accept it, and not even talk to him about it. We have had two good nights of sleep—don't know why, but just grateful!

06.19.08   New Bible study started Tuesday; Marianne is leading it. It is on being a true disciple of Christ and counting the cost. Why are we not taught early on that being a Christian truly means giving up *self* to follow Him? It is clear enough in His teachings, but not preached and taught clearly! (Or maybe, I am not hearing clearly!) My Renovaré assignment is to journal my confessions: I need to confess and repent of my self-centered life. I want to control my environment, including John, Louise, my hours and my activities. Seems the only people I am willing to "put myself out" for are my daughters and my grandchildren. I want to truly see myself as a servant of Christ: serving John, his mother, and paying more attention to my mother. I want to be willing to give up my own time and energy to be the wife John needs at this time. I pray that the Holy Spirit will fill me and use me for God's purposes, and not my own! Thank you, Father, for Donna so willingly taking on the responsibility of the Welcoming Women committee! I pray that I can also turn over the financial responsibilities I have for Women's Spring conference and the Women's Ministry, if that is Your will. I am Yours, Father, and want to serve You with all my heart, mind, soul and strength.

06.23.08   Stan preached a wonderful message on living for Christ, and giving up self (see 06.19 above!) I am reading MacArthur's *Twelve Ordinary Men*—same subject! just finished Murray's *Experiencing the Holy Spirit*—same subject! Now if I will only apply this knowledge in my life and allow God to work through me. We had quite a weekend. Decided Friday to take a picnic to Fairystone Park and rent a kayak. After almost an hour of kayaking and enjoying the lake, we realized the kayak was taking on water where air should be! We capsized and had to call for help while swimming with the upside down kayak! Two fishermen finally heard us and came along to assist us in getting back to boat dock. Lost John's wallet with $200 in bottom of lake! Exciting and fun except for losing the money! Saturday morning, I had the prayer group here for breakfast; ate on porch - nice! Went to Sunday School class picnic Saturday evening; also a nice time. Rested Sunday! Praying for rain; wondering why it rained all around us, but not on us. Finally Sunday night God blessed us with lots of rain—big storm! Thanks!

06.30.08   Have been able to spend some "quality time" with God over the past week, just sitting on the porch, watching the sky and clouds, praying for rain. Thank you, Lord, for the showers. and for the great messages from Larry (AM: faith and works from James) and Stan (PM: How to be people of the Book)—powerful! and Thank You, Lord for Nancy's house in NC finally selling. She lost lots of money on it, but the market is way down. Also, thank you, Father, for teaching me an important lesson today: Had plans to grocery shop for Louise, take breakfast and eat with her at her apartment. Woke up resentful about having to do that... God reminded me that if it were Dottie or any other widow at church, I would be glad to help. So I determined to look at it from James' perspective: true religion is this: Look out for widows and orphans! and went with *joy*! Even patiently took her shopping after we had done her grocery shopping. And felt God' pleasure then and all day since!

Rainbow, rainbows! Almost everyday! Praise to God for His creation! Beautiful skies, clouds, and sunshine, rain and rainbows!

07.05.08   Tuesday Bible study; then hiking with Betty. Then later, hiking with Suz and Joyce and Renovaré meeting in the park, on to grocery store, then home until Sunday! I love being at home, but need to get out every few days. Spent lots of time in yard and garden, and love that. Helping Susan paint fence; wish that did not hurt my wrist, elbow and shoulder so much. Felt out of sorts Friday; newspaper full of bad economic news. Rather depressing; have to remind myself Who is in charge! I thank Him for rain showers last night! I am noticing more and more that I am having a hard time concentrating when I read. My mind wanders so much. John is spending hours in the basement, in his workshop; I wonder if he is just wanting to watch TV and not bother me, or *not* wanting to be with me when I am in a bad mood. convicting! I called Sally and she perked me up. Can't wait to see them!

Oh, the ups and downs!

07.08.08   New symptoms of his dementia? Saturday night
around midnight, he woke in a fright, crying out to God in anguish:
"Help me, Lord!" pulling at the sheets, trying to flip mattress. I
took his hand, telling him that he was having another episode, to
come back to bed. He said he needed to go to the bathroom first.
He headed toward the bathroom, standing in the doorway, he
was peeing as if at the toilet. I turned on the light and saw the wet
floors, bedroom and bathroom and began mopping up. He went
back to bed. I couldn't get back to sleep for a couple of hours. he
saw the cloths and towels next morning and kept apologizing. Not
sure how much he remembered. All OK Sunday and Sunday night.
Sally and kids got here about 5:30 Monday. Sue and Roger came

up and we all enjoyed dinner together. Sally and I sat up till 11:00
PM. When I went in to go to bed, John was standing at the tub in
a peeing position. I told him not to pee in the tub, and he said he
hadn't started yet, went on to toilet, did not remember anything
this morning. Thank You, Lord, for giving me patience in both
these times.

07.24.08   Beautiful morning! Cool and sunny and clear. Wish
we had had more rain as the front passed through; we need several
days of good rain. Continue to pray for rain, horses to sell, and
Nancy's Salem house to sell. My "old-age" physical ailments are
really bothering me lately: achy back, ankles, neck, hands—arthri-
tis? I have had chest pains lately, but attribute those to hard work
outside. Still experiencing slightly upset stomach often. I quit
drinking orange juice in the morning, but not sure how much that
helps. OK, enough griping... finished the Tuesday morning study
on discipleship; a really good study! Very convicting, especially
about being willing to die to self to serve God. Spent several hours
this morning on church clerk business. Should be getting the
report for the 07–08 year to fill out.

07.27.08   Have enjoyed this afternoon on the back porch,
praying for rain! Had Gary and Margie, and Sue and Roger, here for
dinner lat night; nice evening; made me miss Grace a lot today. For
my Renovaré assignment this week, I am to set aside one hour for
worship, just God and me. I am 40 minutes into the hour and lov-

ing it. I am using the July issue of "Today in the Word" devotional from Philippians, so edifying I want to make notes from it.

> And I am sure of this, that he who began a good work in you will bring it to completion at the day of Jesus Christ. (Phil. 1:6)

> And it is my prayer that your love may abound more and more, with knowledge and all discernment. (Phil. 1:9)

> I know how to be brought low, and I know how to abound. In any and every circumstance, I have learned the secret of facing plenty and hunger, abundance and need. (Phil. 4:12)

> For to me to live is Christ, and to die is gain. (Phil. 1:21)

> Only let your manner of life be worthy of the gospel of Christ, so that whether I come and see you or am absent, I may hear of you that you are standing firm in one spirit, with one mind striving side by side for the faith of the gospel. (Phil 1:27)

> Do nothing from rivalry or conceit, but in humility count others more significant than yourselves. (Phil. 2:3)

> Have this mind among yourselves, which is yours in Christ Jesus, who, though he was in the form of God, did not count equality with God a thing to be grasped. (Phil. 2:5)

For we are his workmanship, created in Christ Jesus for good

works, which God prepared beforehand, that we should walk in

them. (Eph. 2:10)

And my God will supply every need of yours according to his

riches in glory in Christ Jesus. (Phil 4:19)

07.31.08   Spent the morning and had nice lunch with Betty.
Talked a lot, but it was therapeutic. What a great friend Betty is!
Took Louise to orthopedic doctor, grocery, balanced her check
book—was exhausted in the evening. John is wandering around
the house at night, so Iam not sleeping. He can't seem to find the
bathroom, then he can't see the bed even when he turns the light
on, just continues wandering. I don't think I sleep more than three
hours at a time.

08.01.08   John took whole pill instead of half pill, and slept!
Also, I put a night light in the bathroom so he goes into the bathroom right away instead of wandering all around. I found a book
in my library by J. Stowell: *The Weight of Your Words*, very timely,
as I work on my "tongue." I know I fail in this area and I know it is
a "heart problem," not just a matter of disciplining my speech, but
changing my spirit. I pray for more love to John, so my speech will
reflect that love, not impatience. I want to stop complaining about
Louise and having to do things for her. I must remember I am serving God in my responsibilities to her, and to John.

Even a fool who keeps silent is considered wise; when he closes his lips, he is deemed intelligent. (Prov. 17:28)

In returning and rest you shall be saved; in quietness and in trust shall be your strength. (Isaiah 30:15b)

08.07.08   Praising God for rain! Hope and pray it lasts all day and more... John's condition: his ability to articulate his thoughts and to understand others is really decreasing. Hard to converse with him and even harder to work with him, not understanding even simple instructions. He watches TV almost all the time, unless he is mowing grass. I sit on the porch and read in evenings; then come in at dusk and sit with him. I re-connected with some Cleveland friends: called Ginny Sunday and enjoyed catching up with her. Then called Jan Tuesday; was able to talk with Hu for a few minutes and with Jan for an hour - wonderful - I miss her friendship, put we picked up right where we left off! Connie and I are trading phone calls; hope to talk to her soon. Not sure what precipitated my desire to reconnect with Cleveland, but I am thankful for old friends. I stay in touch with Barbara, and through her, the K-group from our Bay Village church.

08.17.08   Connie and I finally connected Monday morning and chatted for over an hour. It has been a good week. Sally and kids and two of their friends were here Tuesday through Friday. They enjoyed horseback riding and swimming and movies at Sue and Roger's! Dempsey fell off Sezorr; scared us all, but unhurt. She got right back on him.

08.19.08   Another wonderful vacation at OBX with the Ewans! Third year at a great house, Beechvue, on Southern Shores oceanfront. Met Kevin and Cori and family at the dunes in Kitty Hawk; fun! Gifts from God: great weather, great ocean waves, dolphins, great lightning show Saturday night; beautiful sunrise as we left Sunday morning. Nigel and Parker are so much fun to be with, riding the waves. Dempsey is a beautiful water sprite—how blessed we are!

09.09.08   Nancy's birthday: John prayed that God would let her Salem house sell today. I called her and she is happy being back in Denver. Thank you, God, for drawing me to Yourself. You gave me love and compassion for Louise last week, and a willingness to schedule a doctor appointment and hair appointment to take her in October. I have begun praying immediately upon awakening, before rising, that I will allow the Holy Spirit to take over my life this day. I will not get up until I believe I have totally turned myself over to Him. What a difference it makes!

09.16.08   Sally's 43rd birthday! We thank God for such a wonderful daughter! I made an appointment this morning with a chiropractor; first time for this kind of doctor! My neck has been hurting and stiff since getting smacked on the back of my head in the ocean. Praying morning and evening and often in between. Not sleeping well, so I am praying often in the night, too. John had a bad dream last night and socked me in the shoulder. ouch. He kicked and pushed me one night couple of weeks ago, dreaming and trying to get out of bed on my side.

09.21.08 Felt almost sick today; unsure why. Have worked hard in yard several days this week. Feel better now, after an enjoyable conversation with Betty about everything from books to body shapes! Went back to chiropractor Thursday: reviewed x-rays; evidently had sustained an injury years ago. Several vertebrae in neck have degenerated. he wants me to come for treatments three times a week for several weeks. The most uncomfortable position is when I am driving. Louise is having some medical issues - sinus infection, actually making her sick. polyp in her nose that needs to be removed. Now trying to schedule her appointments and mine so not to conflict.

I talked to Mother a couple of times; she is always sweet. A new term for some forms of dementia: "pleasantly demented"—that's her! and John, too. He has such a sweet disposition, and wants so much to help wherever he can. I got angry with him Friday, then felt terrible and apologized. Thank God (and John) for being forgiving!

And now a few words about our economy: Scary! Exciting! Are

we seeing events of the last days?! Or just a mess from decades

of greed? US problems have expanded into worldwide problems.

Praise God that He is in control—our role is to be obedient to

His word.

Another year of growing and learning

09.26.08   My 66th birthday: worked in garden in morning. Brenda called to wish me a happy birthday. Mother called, worried about her checking account. Talked to Cheri; Joyce called. Sally and kids called and sang to me! Went to Roanoke to take Louise out to eat and to grocery. Then to church. Prayer meeting friends sang *Happy Birthday* to me! Susan and I went out to lunch and to get haircuts on her birthday on the 25th. Then she came up and had dinner with us. She and I worked on a bed skirt for awhile.

For some reason, I woke up unhappy and agitated this morning. I am taking 15 minutes away from my study of Revelation to write and seek comfort from the Holy spirit. Rain and wind kept me awake a lot last night; still pouring rain, thank You, Lord! Nancy just called; she has an offer on the house in Salem, will lose big bucks on it, too. But in this economic turmoil, she just needs to get rid of it. Still praying for horses to sell, and for my neck to be well. So much to do today to get ready for luncheon tomorrow. Oh how I need God, and His peace in my heart!

I am so concerned that my mind is beginning to deteriorate (like my neck!?) When Susan and I were working on the bed skirt last night, I felt like I couldn't concentrate on how to cut or sew it. Lately, also, I am having trouble retaining what I am reading. I try not to worry but I need to be alert and wise to take care of us and Louise. God help me!

09.30.08   Another melt-down yesterday; can't remember when the last one was. I feel frustrated, angry, scared, over-whelmed, etc. Not sleeping well, unable to communicate well with John. He mowed down a small tree; tore up about 15x15 section of the yard "digging up rocks," turf and all. I do not want to have to worry about lawn and trees and shrubs! I calmed down after and 30 minutes of screaming in prayer and anger—calling on God to help me! help me! This came on suddenly after a good weekend. Had a nice birthday dinner at Margie's and Gary's—missed Grace—glad the friendship continues.

10.01.08   Went to chiropractor for sixth time yesterday; seems to be some better, except when driving. Met Joyce S. for lunch before our Renovaré meeting. Told her about my melt-down yesterday - near tears. As each person reported their walk with God during the meeting, I felt I just could not share my weakness. At one point, Joyce called for prayer for me and they all came around me and each one prayed for me. I cried again, then I shared with them the previous journal pages. What an outpouring of love and compassion from these "sisters" of mine!

10.14.08   Had great visit with Ewans. Glad the boys' birthdays are in October; fall foliage was beautiful and the weather nice! Read Piper's *Don't Waste Your Life* (a gift from Brenda). Very convicting!

10.17.08   Oh heavenly Father, how I keep failing in patience! Forgive me! John has lost his wallet again. After helping him look through every drawer and cabinet he might have put it in, I went into his closet. complete mess! I spent over an hour organizing it, getting angrier and angrier, at the mess mostly. God, please help us find it! I cancelled the Visa card; will reorder bank card, etc.

10.25.08   Never did find John's wallet; hope it is in the house and will turn up. Had a weird experience with Louise Wednesday; couldn't understand her voice on the phone (realized later her "teeth" were out) but by the time we got there, she seemed

OK. Need to pray for God's direction for her: apartment or nursing home? I have discovered that when I remember to turn my day and my life over to God before I get up, He is with me and in me that day. So it has been a good week!

10.27.08   Wonderful service yesterday! A tribute to Larry and Ginger, and glory and honor to God. Nice afternoon—took a walk, then made applesauce with John (!). Went to bed around 10 PM; then about 1 AM, he started pummeling me, jerking and pulling on me. I struggled to get him off me; was finally able to slip out on the other side of the bed. He went into his closet and started getting dressed. I asked him where he was going several times; he finally said, "to town," I asked which town, and he said "Roanoke." I asked him how he planned to get there; he responded (always slow responses, and confused), "by bike." I reminded him we do not have bikes anymore, so he motioned toward outdoors and said, "There are guys out there; I'll just go with them." I went back to bed, but watched to see what he would do. He came in by the bed, and said he was not going, there was no way for him to get there. Even after he undressed and got ready for bed again, he kept going back and forth from the bedroom to the bath, turning lights on and off. Finally back in bed - all this in one half hour. I couldn't get back to sleep, was too agitated. But was finally able to sleep some and got up at 7:45 AM. (Late for me!) He could only remember that "something happened in the night" and said he was sorry. I will start sleeping in a guest bedroom; I told him I need rest to stay healthy.

I almost dread our trip to Florida. Please, God, help us to enjoy it
and all to go well.

10.28.08   Realized last evening that John had not been using
the pill container for his meds. Spent half an hour trying to help
him understand it's use. Not sure yet that he does. He is starting to
drive me crazy (sorry, but that is the truth) watching me, following me, pacing around the house. I am glad we set up a little area
downstairs where he can watch TV comfortably during the day.
I slept in guest bedroom last night and rested better. Woke up a
couple times, but was able to go back to sleep.

11.01.08   We winterized the vegetable garden yesterday ; it
was a beautiful day to be outside! We are ready to go to Raleigh and
on to Florida. John is eager to leave now (1 PM) but it is less than
three hours and we are to meet Donna and Pat at 6 PM. I do pray
we will be able to do without a car this week; that will be vacation
for me! I pray we have nice weather and enjoy each other.

11.03.08   We're here! We met Donna and Pat at 6:00. They
took us out to a nice restaurant, Bogart's in downtown Raleigh.
It was so nice to be with them again. By the time we boarded the
train—after 9:30—we were ready for bed, even though we had an
extra hour due to daylight savings. Fun sleeping on train; I took
tiny upper berth (Roger would have been miserable!) Movement
of train was nice, but blowing horn often kept us awake. Taxi from

depot to Star Island was $33! Not *that* far to get there! We were
able to check in early, for which we were grateful. Dinner at TGI
Friday's; music so loud we just brought our salads back to condo to
eat! We are getting old, I guess; we do not like loud music, which is
everywhere! This condo is really nice. I am sitting on the deck and
all I hear are the water fountains. We spent a couple of hours with
the Wyndham people to "update" us (read: try to sell more!) She
was helpful anyway! Then we walked around the Kissimee area
for a couple of hours; got a few groceries. Came back after a huge
breakfast at Perkins—pretty hot here by then. Got in hot tub in
condo. Bonnie and Bill are meeting us at Olive Garden Wednesday!

11.05.08   Lazy day yesterday; walked to Denny's for lunch;
hope to play some tennis. John has been sweet to be with; he has
been pretty confused and "out of it," too. New president: Obama
won. Have been reading books of prophecy at the end of Old Testa-
ment. God's warning to them are so applicable to us today. We
robbed God, we did not help the poor: now our government will
take our wealth and spread it around, unfairly, but that is our due.
We as Americans are rich, proud, and selfish. Now we pay. It will be
interesting to see what transpires in the US with this
new administration...

11.06.08   John and I "played" tennis yesterday; it felt good to
hit that ball again! he did not do well, but was a really good sport
about it. We went for a walk around the grounds later; watched

TV; I worked on my Precepts study and then studied Isaiah awhile. We met Bonnie and Bill at Olive Garden; so nice to be with them! "Played" at tennis again this morning. Went for a walk, then lunch at Friday's. Hot tub again in afternoon. Studying Revelation several hours today. Time is creeping here; I guess because we are not busy. It is nice and relaxing. John seems to be getting worse daily; really forgetful and barely able to process information or to coherently ask questions. He is very loving and sweet.

11.09.08   Spent Friday "hanging out" around the resort, after checking out at 10:00. Beautiful day! Had nicer accommodations on train going back. John seemed really out of it, but not unhappy. Several times he would be talking to me as if I were someone else; then would recognize me and laugh at himself. He did not sleep much (nor did I!) coming back. We had dinner in the dining car. I took top berth again, since he goes to the bathroom often during the night. He went at least ten times and every time I looked down at his bed, he was sitting up, fully dressed. He kept asking where our luggage was. After not sleeping much, we were both really tired Saturday; got home by 3 PM. I got upset with him for not unpacking, not thinking, messed up closet, etc. etc. Felt awful about it. Susan and Roger had us down for supper; went to bed early and slept well. Great worship this morning.

11.10.08   I've been sleeping in guest bedroom; I rest better, but I miss sleeping with John. Woke up early today, feeling really jittery. Turned over myself and the day to You, Lord...

11.23.08   John had episodes three nights in a row. I slept in guest room, but went back to our bed last night, which went fine. It was a good week. Took Louise to dinner Wednesday night; then visited Mother while Susan was at her board meeting. So long as I remember to pray and give myself over to God, every morning, I do OK. Financial situation is getting worse; no one in government seems to have the wisdom to know what to do.

11.28.08   A nice Thanksgiving, after a rough Wednesday! Both mothers, Nancy, Cheri and Rafael, Roger and Susan, Gary and Margie. Roger's parents and his sister and family came for dessert with us. We are having Thanksgiving dinner with them today! I feel so tired so often lately. I sleep OK most nights, but feel tired and sleepy during the day.

12.01.08   Sitting at kitchen table 9 AM; working on Revelations timeline. Feeling mellow, but tired again. My forearms ache (I don't know why) and I woke up in the night and could not go back to sleep. Finished reading Alcorn's *Heaven* last night; wow, a revelation! Never realized how much there is in the Bible about heaven! I've always looked forward to being in heaven, now more than ever!

Hallucinations

12.02.08   John was hallucinating last night. he fell asleep on the sofa watching TV; woke up, got up and walked over to my chair, stepping "over" the patterns in the rug as if they were 3D. At 9:00, he started putting on his shoes and picked up his jacket. I asked him where he was going: he thought/saw? there was a "crowd" in the room, and was going wherever they were going, then maybe going home. Did not know he was at home; thought he lived in Roanoke. "Saw" more people on back porch and kept tying his shoes to get ready to go with them. Never seemed to understand where he was or what was going on. He got irritated with me for asking him questions. Maybe I should have accepted what he was saying? I felt as if I had really lost him. He is very quiet this morning. TV guy

came to fix his TV downstairs; John told the guy he has "degenera-
tive," I guess he forgot the word "dementia."

12.08.08   Continuation of hallucinations; preparing to go out
and/or wondering whose house we are in.

12.22.08   Seems things have been better for John the last
couple of weeks. Thank you, God. No more of the hallucinating;
sleeping better. Still difficult to converse with him. Betty was so
sweet with him in Williamsburg last week; that probably relaxed
him. Sometimes I think my questions and impatience only make
him worse. Our services at church yesterday were so wonderful
and worshipful. Praise God. Beautiful music and messages.

12.30.08   I pray that my mind stays focused as I write one of
the last entries in this 2008 journal. I have so many thoughts rush-
ing around in my head right now, as we prepare to enter a new year.
Trying to write chronologically. We had Susan and Roger here for
our "Christmas dinner on Saturday Dec. 20; asked Susan if she
would be willing to be executor and POA for me. Sally had agreed
with this in earlier phone conversation. Appointment set with our
lawyer for Jan. 29. Had mixed emotions about going to Columbus
again for Christmas: we have spent every Christmas with Sally and
Chip since they have been married. This was Susan and Roger's
third Christmas here and we always leave. Maybe next year we
will stay here, and go to Columbus after Dec. 25.

12.23.10   We took Louise to breakfast before leaving for
Ohio; also went by to see Mother. She smiled and hugged me, then
asked: "Do I know you?" I said, "I sure hope so!" Then she asked if I
was Nancy? Cheri? Joyce? hesitated a minute and asked, "Anne?"

She is so sweet and loving and kind it is hard to get upset with her,
just sad for her. We got to Columbus around 4:00. Sally and I spent
a couple hours at Jeanne's, discussing faith and churches. Wonderful time with the Ewans—how we love them, and thank God
for them! We gave Dempsey a doll and fabric to make clothes for
it. Dempsey and I enjoyed that! I gave Parker my laptop, and gave
Nigel a teapot and money!

Nice drive home on Saturday. John did very well on this trip,
thanks be to God! We got home around 4:00, tired and happy! Sally
had checked out a book at their library about caring for a man with
dementia. I could really relate to the writer. One comment made
me think of Mother's condition: with no memory and awareness,
she can take pleasure in the experience of each moment before
promptly quickly it. So we should be honored to give Mother these
moments of pleasure and not be upset that she cannot remember
us or when we visit or call her. Reading that book and relating to
the writer's feelings makes me realize how support groups
can help.

Mark brought the message Sunday morning, from Psalm 42-43;
God spoke to me through his message and the Psalms! I hope I
can recall all I learned, to refer to when times are hard. I love the
Scripture, even though I don't have the enemies David wrote about.
I do long for God as a deer pants for water, and I do ask my soul why
it is disquieted in me. I want to memorize those chapters; I need
them. I also thought about the fact that Mother is now able to live
for God, pray, read, etc. with no responsibilities or interruptions,
and how blessed that is to spend her last years with Him... and
then realized: as can I! I can refuse to be resentful of having to be
with John 24/7 and can use this time to serve God by serving John,
to read His Word, and rest in Him as I go about my daily routine.
What a blessing! I can look at our duty to Louise as another way to
honor God, and do it with a cheerful heart. I had the opportunity
to do just that yesterday: errand at Lowe's for her, met with lawyer
to change her POA to me, not John, met with Social Security to
make me her "agent" for Social Security and Medicare, took her to
lunch and grocery store, took John to dentist to fix broken tooth
and cap, home at 5:00; wiped out, but in good spirits!

12.31.08   A beautiful day! Billions of stars in the sky when
I went out to get the paper. Now blue sky with billions of crows
flying around! Cold and windy. John seemed to regress a lot yesterday; hard time with TV and everything that was connected to
thinking. Too busy a day yesterday? I have been thinking of Grace

often during this season; remembering her lovely smile and her hospitality. I miss her!

Our "New Year's celebration" was dinner mid-day with Betty and Susan and Roger. We played Chronology after dinner and enjoyed our time together. John seemed content; led us in the blessing and was pretty quiet; watched us play rather than joining in. Then he and I had a quiet evening before retiring to bed at 9:30!

Goodbye to a rollercoaster 2008! Economy, emotions, weather, etc!

What a way to begin a new year

01.01.09   What a difference one day makes ... Yesterday, even this morning, I was feeling great—really able to handle this situation with John's dementia. We got up, had a nice breakfast, read Bible and prayed together, read newspaper—I began doing some cleaning up, getting drawers and closets organized and throwing things out. Had a nice lunch. Went down to see about the TV remote a couple of times for John. I had told him a number of times *not* to touch the buttons or remote except on, off, volume and channels, even put a piece of paper over the mid-section to remind him. Here he comes to me again (ten times in last few days!) asking unintelligible questions about TV remote—I blew up. After true "hissy fit," I went down to basement to see what he needed: the TV was on to his football games! Hallucinating about it? who knows? I cried, screamed, prayed in anguish for help from Jesus. Finally calmed down (thought I was having a nervous breakdown) and went for a walk. OK now, but so ashamed of my lack of patience and lack of control... Talked to Sally, then Joyce—that helped. Hope this evening goes better.

01.03.09   My answer to prayer was to get a really bad case of laryngitis Friday! Can barely speak above a whisper—what a way to keep my mouth shut! Does God have a sense of humor?! I feel all achy—maybe flu? John has a bad cold. I am irritable and impatient. He was drinking coffee at breakfast, choked and spit up coffee over half the kitchen—kept walking as he was choking! I was furious that he didn't stay in one place but kept quiet since it hurts to talk. I cleaned it up. He read most of our Bible reading yesterday and today; so sad, he reads like a 2nd grader. But God hears him and knows his heart....

01.04.09   Oh woe is us—but God is good: while reading 2 Corinthians 4, He spoke to me: "We are afflicted in every way, but not crushed; perplexed, but not driven to despair; [sometimes!] persecuted, but not forsaken; struck down, but not destroyed [...] So we do not lose heart. Though our outer self is wasting away, our inner self is being renewed day by day. For this light momentary affliction is preparing for us an eternal weight of glory beyond all comparison, as we look not to the things that are seen but to the things that are unseen. For the things that are seen are transient, but the things that are unseen are eternal." After reading that passage and praying for the Holy Spirit to make it alive for us, went for a walk in much better spirits. (Spirit!?) Didn't sleep well Saturday night; fitful sleeping for some reason. John woke me up at 3:30 AM to ask if I would drive him to church Sunday morning! I felt terrible—achy, throat still sore. But we started out—dropped off trash at dump and book at library—got within a half mile of church and he realized he had lost his wallet. Retraced our steps—no wallet—got home and had phone call from finder of wallet; met him at dump and profusely thanked him. He would not accept any reward money. Rested in afternoon and evening.

01.05.09   Rainy day today. We see bluebirds at birdhouse—how beautiful! Voice still rough, throat hurts, praying I get ok by Thursday's Bible study.

01.10.09   My sore throat lasted one week before it turned into a cold. I took med this morning and feel pretty good now. cleaned house and went for walk with John. We have begun to take trash bags and clean up the trash on sides of our road when we walk. John is hallucinating again; thought a man was in our bedroom snoring Monday night! I realized today that he is having difficulty using the phone now. I asked for prayer for him Wednesday night and several people lifted us both up in prayer. What a blessing... Started the 3rd Revelation study yesterday and will start teaching the Sunday School class for Audrey P this Sunday. Rafael's mother died Wednesday of cancer. We offered to go to Charlotte for the funeral, but Cheri said no. Just as well, with neither John nor I feeling well.

John seems to think someone else lives with us. He is frequently referencing "the other young (ha!) lady..." when it was me telling him something. He often speaks to me and someone else when we are alone, even looks to my side as if someone is there. When we had gone to bed last night—I had stayed up and read for another half hour or so—he rose up from the pillow and asked me, "What are you doing up here?" I said, "going to bed to sleep." He said, "I was worried about you down there." Not sure what makes him use "up" and "down" ...About 4 AM, after restless hours for both of us due to colds, he got up and got dressed. He tapped me on the shoulder and said, "Anne, Anne, are you planning on coming back up here?" I told him to go back to bed, and he did. I realized later he was fully dressed, and had put his shoes on the bed at his pillow. When I asked him about his shoes, he said, "Someone lectured me about not putting my shoes so close to the bed." (I had asked him several times not to put his shoes against the white bedskirt!) I still find myself getting very frustrated with him, even when I know, in my mind, he cannot help it. I keep thinking about nursing homes, but I really don't want to do that until I can't handle him.

01.12.09   Another middle of night/early Sunday morning episode of getting up and getting dressed. I took a sleeping pill last night and slept through till about 9 AM; don't know if he got up or not... Kris and Tom came for lunch Saturday—had Susan and Roger up for dessert with us. Wonderful worship on Sunday! Stan taught us about marriage from various Scripture; also used the John Piper book on marriage that Sally gave me for Christmas. A Christian psychologist spoke Sunday night from Ephesians 4:25–32. Both very convicting. Does God want me to devote all my time and energy to John right now? Is that the role of a good wife? I know I need some rest and respite, but how much?

01.18.09   It has been a good week; we have both slept well and enjoyed time together. We helped Susan with the horses; Roger was in D.C. Monday through Friday. It was really cold all week; Renovaré here on Tuesday; Wednesday John and I ran errands and ate dinner out before church. Such loving prayers for us are said at prayer meeting. What a blessing is our church family! Thank you, Lord! Precept Thurs went well; had a chance to spend some time with Cathy before going to Roanoke to take Louise to the doctor and to grocery store. Was uneasy about leaving John that long, but he seemed to do ok; even heated soup and made himself a sandwich. He is experiencing "sundown syndrome" now: disoriented, confused in the evenings. When he does a task, he needs directions one at a time; cannot process more than one thing at a time. I find things out of place often. He wants to help, but usually creates

more work for me. We had Larry and Ginger here for lunch Sat;
that was so enjoyable! He brought me a book that Randy had given
him two of John Frame's *The Doctrine of God*—heavy theological
tome! Another great message from Stan today on parenting. Praise
God for how Sally and Chip are parenting!

Renovaré assignment was to write a prayer to God:

> Dear Father,
>
> I sit here this evening, with a quiet heart. I think of the Scrip-
> ture "Thou will keep him in perfect peace, whose mind is stayed
> on Thee." Thank you, my Father, for this peace of mind. It is so
> welcome after months of unease and disquiet in my soul. (Ps 42)
> Maybe I have finally reached the acceptance of mine and John's
> new life—just love him and take care of him—Marriage is from
> God; marriage is to honor God. Thanks to John Piper; thanks to
> Stan—a real turning point. Father, help me always to be open to
> your Word and to be obedient. I desire to love you and serve you,
> with all my heart, soul, mind, and strength.
>
> Your daughter, Anne

01.21.09   John is 67 today; I wonder what his 68th birthday
will be like. It seems his dementia has progressed at double-pace
since the New Year. He has lost so many everyday words and his
ability to understand normal conversation is so poor. We went to
Ohio, and he seemed fine there—kinda dazed acting, but slept well.

After we got back home, he seems more confused and less able to express himself verbally. I can understand about 50% of what he is saying. He has lost so many words, and is so directionally-impaired. He is having more hallucinations; thinks he is somewhere besides home, thinks there are other people in the house, etc. It is scary.

01.22.09   Memo to Sally:

He found it in his closet, I think. (he had lost his wallet). I was in the kitchen, and heard him say, "I found it", so I did not ask.

At the cafeteria yesterday, I noticed that he had hooked the chain on it to the other end of it, not to his belt loop. So I told him he ought to hook it to his belt loop. Louise chimed in, telling him as well. He re-hooked it to itself again, and we both again told him to be sure to hook it to his belt loop. By this time, he was getting agitated with us, and I noticed that again, he had not done it right, but did not say anything else. So I was afraid he had lost it yesterday in the cafe, or Kroger, or at his Mom's, etc...

He lost his razor, and I found it in his Awana briefcase.

He has lost so many words. He called wallet "moneybelt" and used sign language of shaving to tell me about the razor being lost.

He got lots of cards from his Master Gardener friends, and had forgotten almost all of them. The names meant nothing to him. His favorite, Kathleen, is coming tomorrow morning to

bring him some award certificates from the chapter. I think he
will know her when he sees her.

We have a doc apptointment for him at noon tomorrow.

Love, Mom

John was so confused last night. I had told him that I planned to
do laundry this morning, which I usually tell him, so he can get his
dirty clothes in the basket. Later we were sitting on the couch, as
usual, me reading, him "watching" TV, and he said he was tired.
It was about 9:30, so I suggested he go on to bed. He asked where
should he go? If he went to the door, was our unit close by? When
I told him this was our house, he asked me if we lived here alone. I
answered yes, just us; was he thinking of the timeshare condos?
IIe said, What about that girl who said she was going to do
the laundry?

I told him I was that "girl." in just a few minutes, he commented,
"Anne got my pills for me today." (Got prescriptions from doctor at
the appointment.) I wanted to cry. I just looked at him, and he said,
oh, yeah, that is you.

01.25.09   Have had an interesting day here: John was up
at 4:45 am, walking around the house, looking for his closet. His
closet is off the master bathroom, and he had closed the door to
it, so I guess he didn't "see" it. I told him what time it was, and to

come back to bed. When he got back in bed, he said "I don't have any clothes here." I said, Yes, you do, a closet full, but you don't need to get up for two hours yet.

We got up about 6:45, and he again started walking all through the house, looking for his closet. I brought him back into our bathroom, and showed him the closet door. He was able to get dressed without any help, but when I came back to see if he was ready for breakfast, he had his razor in his hand, preparing to put it in his pocket. I asked what he was doing with it, and he said, he wanted to take it home. I reminded him that we were at home, and he was totally confused. Then he got out his Awana briefcase to take to church, and I reminded him he did not need it til Wednesday night...

While he was taking up the offering in church, he dropped all the money and envelopes out of his plate, and had to stop and pick it up.

After we got home, we were sitting by the fire in the living room, and he stood up, and asked if he had brought a coat in. I said no, he had not. He looked around, then went to the front door, and said, "Well, have a good day." and walked out. I watched, and he just walked around the yard, then came in through the garage. We tried to talk about the whys and whats, but he did not know anything, so we dropped it.

He is often confused where he is; seems not to realize this is our house, and no one else lives here. He often uses plural when asking me something about what we are doing, as if I have someone else here. A friend of Susan's brought me the book *The 36-Hour Day*, about caregiving for dementia patients. He looks through it, and asks me questions about it.

With him having left the house, and not knowing where he was, or where he was going, I guess I will not be able to leave him alone anymore.

Uplifting responses from Christian sisters

My Sister,

    What can I do to help? It discourages me that such a beautiful, Godly, Christian couple would have to suffer like this. Please let Melvin and myself know what we can do to make your load lighter.

I love you,

    Vickie

Wow Anne. I am crying with what I just read. I just can't even begin to imagine how hard it is for you to watch John deteriorate like this. Please know that I am praying for you and John that the Lord would give you peace and grace and that you would feel His presence in the midst of all of this.

Please let me know if there is anything I can do for you or any ways I can help you. You are so special to me.

Love,
Jenny

Oh Anne, I can't believe all that! It is so heart-breaking. Bless his heart and bless yours. I pray for God's extra measure of patience and strength and peace for you during these days. Thank you for sharing that with us so that we can pray appropriately for you. You are not alone. You and John are loved and I believe that the Lord is going to show Himself to be very real to you. I pray that you will see specific answers to prayer in order to increase your faith and your ability to trust God. I am praying for that at this very moment.

In His Love...
Tara

Anne, I am praying and if I can do anything at all it would be an honor. I love you both! I will not be going to Becky's today. Let's keep in touch.

Suz

John and I both had a really rough morning. We got up at 6:45, and I felt stressed as I got up from the bed, and prayed for guidance and patience as I was rising. That didn't last long: I was throwing a load of clothes in the wash hurriedly to go prepare breakfast, and he tried to kiss me and I pulled away. I saw the hurt in his eyes, and felt awful. But did not say anything...

He is 100% more needy in the kissy, huggy, etc. area now, and I want to just shrug him off. I sit with him in the evenings, and he rubs my back for hours; I can't believe I get tired of that! He wants to kiss and kiss and kiss when we go to bed, and I usually back off, or ask God to make him back off.

After breakfast, we had our Bible reading and prayer time, and as usual, I implored God to *make* me be who He wants me to be. I pray that every day, and I fail every day. I had written out the tasks I need to do today, and started on several of them, tripping over myself in my haste and impatience. He wants so much to help, but only gets in the way, and I have to re-do much of what he does. So I only made him feel worse.....

When I sat down to work on my Precept study for this week, I
could not concentrate, or even understand the Scripture, and ended up sobbing and praying for half an hour. Maybe I need to give
up teaching Precept. Kris is willing to take over for me, but has not
been "Precept trained", although she has checked out the training
schedule and is willing to be trained. Another stumbling block is
that she and Tom have not joined the church, and I am not sure she
will be "allowed" to teach. I have an email in to Pastor Mark to ask
him what the policy is on that. I asked God in my anguish if I could
put out a fleece (Gideon), that if Mark says it is ok for Kris to teach,
will that be my ok from Him (God). I'd like to be sure of what God
wants of me.

John and I talked about this at lunch and went for a walk; he keeps
saying he thought wc could "get through this." and I asked if he
meant Get well. He said no, not be healed, just get through it together. I told him we will, and we can, with God's help; that maybe
we need to recognize that we will also have some difficult days in
this journey. I know that God has given us this trial for a reason:
for our spiritual growth, to grow closer to Him and to each other,
and to bring glory to Him.

01.27.09   We had to cancel our Renovaré meeting today
because of inclement weather; I was so sorry not to be able to
meet with my "sisters." John and I had a good day here at home; I
worked in the sewing room, cleaning out boxes and trying to orga-

nize old Bible study material, and old tax papers, and photos. More to do there! He helped by gathering up the trash I was accumulating. The only odd things today: at breakfast, he mentioned that he wished he had his two heavy jackets here, as if we were not at home. I reminded him that all his clothes were here, we were at our house. Then tonight in the living room, he asked me if I had had a good trip here today. I reminded him that we had both been here all day. He looked puzzled, then said, "I know that!" I am not sure I am doing the right thing by "reminding him," instead of just agreeing with him.

01.29.09 Did not have Awana at church last night, so we did not go. Today is a beautiful, even though cold, day, so we did have Precept class. I talked to John yesterday about my need for uninterrupted time to study (he comes in and starts talking at any time; he did not used to do that, he used to be able to tell I was studying.) In a few minutes, he came in and whispered a question to me. I guess he thought if he whispered, it would not be bothering me! Then this morning, he was whispering to me when we got up. I asked him why he was whispering, and he said that he did not know if "the others" were up yet. I told him we were home alone. Then he asked if I had seen a small satchel; I asked if he had lost his Awana bag. He had a hard time telling me no, but he needed one to put some clothes in, for when he went "over there", and pointed outside. He said he did not have one yesterday and needed one to take a change of clothes in when he went there, and pointed toward the north side of the house. I told him that we did not even go outside yesterday, that the weather was bad. I also told him that these questions are the reason that dementia patients should not be left at home alone, and maybe I should not go to church this morning. He assured me he would be fine, and when I got home, he seemed to be ok.

He gets lost in the house, cannot remember where his closet is, or maybe, can't remember what "closet" means...

I heard from Pastor Mark that Kris cannot teach until she is a member of the church, so I told him about my "fleece" and that I guess this is God's telling me to keep teaching this class.

01.30.09   Had a nice day; left home about 9:30 to go pick up Louise and take her to grocery. Saw Billie at grocery; couldn't help but wonder why SHE can't take Louise when she goes. Left John with Louise and met Betty; we went to a great little restaurant in Grandin Village. Then shopping for a picture for over our bed; did not find anything.

01.31.09   Started out a nice day; got my Bible study for Sunday School done; talked to Joyce and to Betty. Made veggie soup for lunch, then John and I went for a walk. When we got back, we went into the woods on our property across the street, to do some clean-up. He used a lopper to cut small saplings down, and I raked.

Enjoyable! Beautiful day. After supper, he started asking questions that did not make sense; it was apparent he did not know he was at home. Asked if he could ride in that thing back to his house; asked if there was a place for him in this house; where should he sleep? what was his room number? etc, etc. I tried to help him with the questions, but could not understand most of them. I stayed calm, but he was really out of it. Finally he went to bed about 8:30.

I am reading *The 36-Hour Day* for caregivers of dementia patients. It is frightening what will be happening to us. God help us both.

02.01.09 Only got about three hours' sleep last night; John was restless; got up about 7 or 8 times, bathroom, putting on/taking off jeans; putting on/taking off socks, etc. About 5 am, he was out of bed, asking me about watching football tonight; he has been paranoid about the Super Bowl game, afraid we could not watch it on our TV, could not get the channel, whatever. I finally got up about 6:00; he was pacing all over the house, turning on lights, etc. I asked him if he knew what was wrong, and again he started in about wanting to go to our house, all his clothes were at our house, etc., but could not tell me which house he meant. He answered that he knew he was at home.

He sometimes refers to me as "ma'am" and sometimes as "you all". At one point he said, "Am I just going nuts?" so he seems to know he is not making sense.

02.03.09   We had a nice Sunday afternoon, although he was confused about this being our house. We watched the Super Bowl game at Susan and Roger's, and enjoyed supper with them.

Monday was a good day; it sure was better for me than last Monday morning! He lost his glasses, but I was sure they were in the house somewhere, and he has two pair, so it was not a big deal. We prayed for God to help us find them, and by Tuesday morning, he found them in a jacket in the car. Monday afternoon, we worked out in the woods in our lot across the street, raking and clearing debris. He was confused a lot, but was able to help with raking. He really wants to use his chain saw, but I keep discouraging him from doing that.

This morning I studied my Revelation lesson, and he was up and down the basement stairs. He "worked on" his John Deere lawn mower tractor, and it was running fine, but now it is not. I wonder what he might have done to it? My Renovaré group met here today, so it was a good day for me. After dinner this evening, John and I were on the sofa, and he turned and asked me where *my* bed is. I said do you mean *our* bed? Where is *your* bed? He pointed to my office, which is not quite the right direction, but at least it was the right side of the house. I walked into our bedroom with him, and he said is this it? I asked him if it did not look familiar to him, and he just said, I guess so, I wanted to be sure. Then he asked me what "she" said about checking out the basement lights, and he looked into our bedroom and said he checked them. I reminded him that I was the "she" who asked, and he should go down into the basement to check the door and the lights. He could not find the way, so I showed him the door to the basement. He went down and came back, and thanked me for showing him how to get there.

Sally had sent me a link to a blog for Alheizmer Spouses, so I went on it and read lots of comments by women whose husbands have this. It made me so thankful to God that John has such a pleasant disposition, that I determined to show more love and tenderness to him. From Sally:

> I thought you might want to see what my friend Julie sent me today:
>
> "How is your week? I've been thinking about your dad and praying. I seem to pray for your mom when I think of your dad. It's just such a hard process for both but your mom remembers the struggles. I know your dad must still be able to sense his decline and I pray that he does not feel so frustrated."
>
> Isn't that sweet? She always asks about you both. I hope you have a good day!
>
> XOOX
>
> Sally

My reply:

How sweet! I appreciate so much all the prayers for us both; please let Julie know.

Yes, as you know, Dad does sense his decline. I see periods of depression (maybe that is too strong a word) in him more often lately. I am trying to encourage him, telling him how much loved he is, and how people often comment on his friendliness and handling of this disease.

It has been so cold the past 3 days, we are not working outside, and I miss that. I went out yesterday, all bundled up, with my garden tools, and came in within 5 minutes! It was about 20!

Gene (his wife Barbara is in Precept) called Tuesday night, and offered to go to breakfast with John today. So he went in to Rocky Mount with me this morning, and we met up with Gene. The guys went to Bojangles' and then to Lowe's, and Gene brought him back to church to meet me. He and I went to Virginia BBQ for lunch and are now back home.

Before Precept this morning, I asked Pastor Mark if he had a few minutes. I told him again how much I wished I could hear a direct response from God about my teaching vs. spending more time with John. He listened well, talked a little about Robinson McQuilken (was that his name?) but Mark could not give me any advice, except to continue as I am for now. He then prayed for us. I am so thankful we are in this church at this time!

We are on our way to Charlotte tomorrow, or rather, to

Denver and to Newton. We plan to be home before dark.

Cheri and I are meeting for lunch next Thursday; it will be nice to see her. I don't think I have seen her since Thanksgiving!

Joyce and I are talking 4 or 5 times a week; Don is now in rehab, and may come home within the next two weeks.

Love, Mom

02.07.09   We had a nice trip yesterday; he is easy to travel with. We went to Nancy's first, to see her new house, and to take her with us to see Jackie. I am so glad we went to see Jackie; she really appreciated it. If she has more strokes, this may be the last time we see her. We took Nancy out to lunch, then were able to get home before dark.

He seemed ok this morning, but as the day wore on, he got more confused. We worked in the woods again this afternoon, for about 3 hours. It was a nice day, and I enjoyed it, but it was exhausting! When we came in, he said he was going to shower. I told him to put his jeans in the dirty clothes. The basket was right next to him. He kept starting to put them down everywhere except in the basket; finally, I pointed to it, and he put the jeans in, and took his shoes out (!) of the basket. Then he picked up a clean pair of briefs and started to put them on. I told him not to put on clean pants until he had finished showering; he thought he needed them on to go to the shower—he had started out the bedroom door by then. I directed him back into the bathroom, and the shower. He took the pants into the shower, I guess thinking it was a washcloth. Later this evening, he said he was going to bed; it was 8:15. He said he was really tired, especially after "those people" told him about showering and what he should do. I did not think it was an especially stressful conversation, but I guess he did. So he is in bed, and I will read the "36 hour day" for awhile tonight. I pray we both get a good night's sleep; last Saturday night was about 3 hours off and on...

02.08.09   We did have a good night's sleep, thank God. Before he went to bed, he had me come into the bedroom, pointed to the bed, and asked if that was where he should go to bed. This morning on the way to church, he was trying to ask me a question, but could not get it out. He mentioned his dad dying at 78, but did not go anywhere with that. Then he mentioned that I was not with him when he lived at the lake. I asked him who did he think cooked his meals! He then said, he must have a big hole in his brain, where all these words fall out. He tried for quite a while to think of whatever his question was, but never did. I was patient the whole time; thank God for that. I am trying to give him my undivided attention, no matter what else I might be doing, when he is talking to me. I feel better about myself, and I know he feels better!

Wonderful friends

02.14.09   This has been a good week. I have come to expect that evenings are difficult: his hallucinations are recurring, and his inability to recognize that this is our home seems worse in the evenings. I just keep reminding myself that he can't help it, and thanking God that he is so sweet. We worked outside for a few hours a couple of days. He has trouble following "instructions" from me, so most of the time, I just let him go, and he rakes where and what he wants to. I know he wants to feel like he is helping, so I have to remember to *let* him "help." I did get upset one morning, when he was insisting that my ring was "by the front door." I knew where I had put it, and he finally saw it by his closet door, bringing it to me on my toothbrush! After getting angry with him, for once again picking things up that do not need to be moved, I cried because I felt so bad for getting angry. We prayed together, and I do thank God that He is forgiving, and that John is forgiving!

We had dinner with the Carrs today, and he enjoyed it. He had a hard time expressing himself, but they were patient, and it was fine.

02.18.09   We had dinner with Ronnie and Rebecca Sunday after church, and enjoyed being with them. We don't know them very well, but I feel close to them because of our being together in prayer meeting every Wednesday night. He was the surveyor for this property when we bought it. John joined in on conversations, but struggled with words; they were very kind and patient.

Monday I worked in the yard for several hours; he joined me for a little while, but stayed inside most of the day. When I came in later in the day, he had taken the grandfather clock apart, and had all the parts lined up on the floor. He admitted he did not know why he did that, and of course, could not get it back together. So now we just have the shell of a clock, with no time or chimes. I am not sure whether I will have the guy come out to fix it, since John may decide to take it apart again.

Tuesday, I had Renovaré, and Susan and I went to lunch before I went to Vickie's. I enjoy Susan; she is a great gal! Thanks to God for such wonderful daughters, and their wonderful husbands! I have been feeling pretty good about my time with John; I think I am more patient. I know I need to watch my facial expressions when he is talking nonsense. Which he is doing more and more often...

We are home today; it is a rainy, cold day outside, and it is nice to be inside with a good book; he is watching TV, and I have had earplugs in so I can read. He asked me to sit down and talk to him for a minute, so I did. He told me he had "some money" and what should he do with it. I knew he had about $25 from the sale of one of his power tools; he had given me the other $100 to hold on to for him. I told him he could put it in his wallet, but to remember to hook the wallet to his belt loop if he takes it with him. He said No, it is a coffee pot. (?) Then he realized that did not make sense, but he could not make sense. I am not yet sure what he meant. I told him I would put the money in my purse for him. He liked that idea, and brought me what he said was "$600". I was shocked, and counted it, and it was only $135. When he handed it to me he said he was uncomfortable with having it, "with that man looking over his shoulder in there." I asked what man, and he said one of those drivers. (?) Then he brought me about $25 more he found in his closet; I guess he has been stashing money away, and is finding it as we pack for the trip to Columbus.

I am still waiting on guidance and wisdom from God about teaching Precept after this class is over March 19th. I feel like I need to be with him all the time, but I do want to stay with the Precept group; they are like a support group for me. Part of our lesson yesterday was from Matthew 25, when Jesus is telling his followers, "Truly, I say to you, as you did it to one of the least of these my brothers, you did it to me." and I wondered if God is telling me to *do for* John, his mother, and mine at this time of our lives...

The man in the mirror

02.24.09   Just got home from a trip to Columbus yesterday
afternoon; had a nice visit with the Ewans. How thankful we are
for them! As usual, John seemed really confused when we got
home. We had stopped in Roanoke to take Louise to the grocery
store, and I thought that might make for an easier transition
for coming home. But he kept trying to ask questions when we
got home, and could not express his thoughts, so it was hard to
help him talk. He doesn't give me enough words to know how to
decipher his thoughts. I have handled things pretty calmly for
several weeks now, and thought we were making great progress in
handling this disease, but had another "melt-down" that evening:

John told me that the squeegee in our shower was gone, so I went in the bathroom to help him find it. I asked him if he could remember the last time he might have used it, and where he *might* have put it (foolish question) and he put his hand on his heart and said he was positive he did not move it. I reminded him that I have had to help him find myriads of things he had misplaced, so I was pretty sure he had just put it somewhere. He continued to "assure" me that he did not move it out of the shower, again and again, until I finally broke, and told him he was a liar. That he knew he was the one in this house who misplaced things over and over. We tried to reason it out, and finally I gave up, and after looking everywhere I could think of in the bathroom and in his closet, I found it in the dirty clothes basket in his closet. He finally agreed that yes, he probably put it there by mistake. I felt awful that I had called him a liar, when he probably was certain in his mind that he was telling the truth, so I apologized to that effect, and we made up. But I still felt terrible, and he did, too.

Before we went to bed last night, he asked me a couple of times where he should sleep, i.e., which bed, which room (unconnected to the earlier episode) ; this goes on frequently. He thinks he is not at home, and therefore, unsure where we are supposed to sleep. He said a couple of times, "Well, I think I will go on across the street. Is it number 5?" getting his shoes to wear outside. There is a vacant lot that we own across the street. He was pretty restless last night, which he usually is after we return from a trip. I did sleep ok, other than between 1:30 and 2:30 or so. This morning, he seemed to want to review some event, and I guessed it was last night's episode, but he kept talking about "couples" and "beds" and "wanting to know what was going on". He could not tell me who, where, or when, and just got more frustrated with himself for not being able to grasp the right thoughts and words to say. I finally asked him if he thought I was seeing someone, since he has mentioned in the past that he sees men here. He did not really answer me, but his face looked like that could be it. I assured him I was not interested in any man, nor even in sex! I am not sure he was satisfied that that was what his concern was, but he dropped it.

02.25.09   I asked for prayer for John at prayer meeting tonight, that he would not be depressed when he realizes how much he has lost. It seemed like five or six people prayed for him, and such warm, heart-felt prayers they were! Thank you, Lord, for such a wonderful church family, who love us, and pray for us both. I felt actually lifted up!

02.26.09   Email from Vickie:

Hi Anne,

I find myself praying for you two at night more often, I hope last night was uneventful.

Reading my BSF notes I came across this and thought of you. We cannot fail to be impressed with how gentle God is with His weary servant. Instead of condemning Moses, He provides help for him. Surely, in the case of God, "a bruised reed he will not break, and a faintly burning wick he will not quench; he will faithfully bring forth justice." (Isaiah 42:3). Indeed, "For he knows our frame; he remembers that we are dust." (Psalm 103:14). Since this is God's character, are you bold in coming to Him in prayer on all occasions? I can't believe these are the very words Pastor Stan used last Sunday in his sermon "Bold Praying".

Love you,

Vickie

My reply:

Thank you, Vickie, for this message, and especially for your prayers. I mentioned your prayer this morning to Stan. (I had asked him for some time to talk about my continuing leading Precept.) I told him that I felt as if I were on a cloud all the way home after prayer meeting last night. Last night was fine; I got a good night's sleep. When we got up this morning, and were making up the bed, John asked me how much will we need to pay for this—waving his hand across the bed, as if we were in a motel. He said there was a man walking around, with an insigna on his shirt (thinking of Awana shirts?) and with cracker jacks. Then he laughed as if he realized that did not make sense, but he still talked about that man. ?

When I got to church this morning, I saw Pastor Doug, and asked teasingly if he would do me a favor. He agreed quickly, without even asking what I needed. I asked if he would go see John this morning. He agreed, and called Donnie Hunley and the two of them came out here and visited with John! They even got our grandfather clock working again! John had taken it apart last week, and could not put it back together.

Stan and I talked for an hour, and he was non-committal for the first part of the discussion. As we continuing talking, he then said that I should not let any of my church responsibilities stand in the way of my taking care of John. But he encouraged me to take care of myself, and I told him about my "care" group, Renovaré. He was aware of our meeting weekly, and encouraged me not to quit that. I told him I could not quit; that is my support; calling attention to your prayer, and how much I need to know that you all are praying for me. He said that was a powerful group of women lifting me up in prayer!

So thanks again for loving and caring for us; I love you so much! I am hoping for some nice days for painting in March. It will be so nice to spend that time with you!

Love,

Anne

02.28.09   A couple of cold, rainy days, so we agreed to clean up the basement. Most of the large power tools have been sold, but there are shelves packed with all kinds of small tools, paint and painting equipment, hundreds of nails, screws, etc., electrical and plumbing items, etc. There are five units for storing small items, with many individual "drawers" in them, all very dirty after being in so many of his shops, with all the sawdust. So I spent hours going through them, dumping them, washing them, and reloading them. John was not much help; he has forgotten what lots of these things are for. We began to build a pile for Roger and his friend Kenny to go through to see if they can use them. It all reminded me of how handy John was before this disease. He had finished our basement at the lake house, including dry wall, paneling, ceiling, ceramic tile flooring, electricity and plumbing. Now we have all those tools sitting useless. I know he is unhappy about not know-ing how to do any of that anymore. I tried to make his "sitting area" down there much neater and cleaner. Evidently at some point, he unloaded the file holding all the info about the tools and other gar-den and household equipment; it was piled up on his desk. I made new folders for much of it, and re-filed it. He seemed to appreciate all this, but did not say much, and I know he did not enjoy the work!

After he took a shower this afternoon, I was in the kitchen baking and cooking for awhile. I came back toward our bedroom, and saw him just sitting in a chair in there, with his eyes huge and staring.

I asked if he were ok, and he said yes. He probably sat there for a couple of hours. That is very unusual for him. Then I called him in for dinner, and he ambled in, still looking lost. He sat down and began eating, after a halting blessing, and then said, "I think I will go on after this." He did not realize we were at home, and even asked me at one point, "Does your husband … ?" and then smiled, and said, "I am your husband." He did not make sense in 75% of what he said this evening. Thank God I was able to be calm, and answer when I could, without being my usual "why?" "what do you mean?" self. It seems to be better for both of us if I just nod and smile when I don't understand him. We were able to joke this morning about his comments last night: he came into the living room after being in our bedroom/bath/closet, and told me he had seen the box car that had clothes in it. Then he corrected himself, and said, "I mean the truck that carries clothes." I asked if he meant "closet" and he just smiled.

03.02.09   Woke up to a beautiful snow this morning; about six inches or so. Church was cancelled last night because of the icy roads, and snow coming down. We had planned to go into Roanoke to take Louise to grocery and to lunch/brunch, but roads were too bad, and she should not be out on the ice anyway. So we saved that for tomorrow, after I rescheduled other events for the next two days! John took the wrong three pills at breakfast, one being Clonazepam for helping him sleep. He has been a basket case today; driving me insane. I hate to say that I lost it twice with him.

He wanted to go out and remove some of the snow, so I asked him to take the chair cushions and shake them, then lay them vertically to dry out. He went out and I could tell he had no idea of what to do, so I stepped out and did the three closest to me, and asked him to do the fourth one. He couldn't even handle that, just looked at them all, and started moving the chairs, not the cushions. So I stepped out again, and did the 4th one, with mutterings and such.

Later, he went out to get the newspaper, and came in with snow all over his jeans, brought his snowy boots inside. I asked him to please go back out and clean off the snow; he could not comprehend what that meant, and started into one of the bedrooms, shaking off the snow. I grabbed a towel and started cleaning up the floor, practically screaming at that point for him to *go outside*! He finally did, after the damage was done. Then he has been pacing all over the house since then, sits and watches TV for a little while, then walks all around again. He just came in and asked if he could shave. I looked at him funny, and told him that he does not need to ask me those kind of questions, he can shave any time. He said he did not know how much longer we would be here. Again, thinking we are not at home. ?

The other day after he showered, he got out and got dressed, but forgot to turn off the shower.

I have checked on adult activity center in Rocky Mount, and he can go there one day a week, if he is self-sufficient. So I plan on taking him there Thursday while I go to church and to get a haircut. He doesn't want to go, but I told him I need him to go; I am afraid to leave him here alone. It has *not* been a good day! of course, Nancy again told me to go on Prozac. I do not want to, but I may need it. Prayer doesn't seem to be enough to calm me down some days.

I asked Karon (Free Clinic Director) and Brenda both what they thought of taking Prozac, and both were strongly positive about it.

03.03.09   A much better day today, thank God. We left this morning to get his hair cut, and ended up at my hairdressers, since his barber shop was closed. Cute haircut, and enjoyed the time with Peggy, who was so sweet to him. Then on in to Roanoke, to get Louise. Thank goodness she knew the icy walks would be danger-ous for her, and did not go out. We shopped for her, and picked up lunch, which happened to be cinnamon rolls instead of burgers when we got back to her apartment! Mistake of Hardee's employee! Wonder what the person thought who got burgers instead of cin-namon buns!

I had a really nice lunch and visit with Nancy and Cheri. Nancy's husband Reid had Lewy Body Dementia, so she is good to talk with; she understands. Cheri is just fun to be with! I love my sis-ters so much, even though we are poles apart politically.

We called Joyce, but got her message service, so we all just said hello into the phone!

03.05.09   email to Sally:

Wednesday afternoon, Dad turned to me and said:

—will you drop me off there on the way back?

—where?

—Uhhhhhhhhhhhhhhhh, I can't think of the name...uhhhhhhhhhh

—Do you have a bag that a t-shirt will fit in?

—the last time you wanted that was to go take a shower; is that what you are thinking?

—I guess...

—Well, you can shower in the bathroom where you always do; you don't need to go anywhere.

—You didn't know my dad did you?

?

—I want to do that; it's not dirty...

?

—I can't drive, so I need a ride.

—Where do you want to go? we are going to church.

—uhhhhhhhhhhhh... I can't think of it...uhhhhh

This went on for over an hour; I was able to be patient all through it, but never did know what he was thinking or what he wanted.

That is why I *do* need time away; it is so tiring!

This evening he came in while I was on the computer, and pointed outside and asked if this was Franklin Rd. (that is a street in Roanoke) I asked him if he knew where he was, and he said "well, I guess this could be my house"

I had tried to get him to go to the Senior center while I was in Bible study, getting my hair cut, and grocery shopping, but he preferred to stay at home. He made himself a peanut butter sandwich for lunch, and seemed to have done OK. Roger came for dinner, and I noticed that John did not talk much at all. When Roger was leaving, he started talking, but not making sense. Roger asked him to come down Friday afternoon to help him move a heavy bench; I am glad John can help. I know he wants to feel needed.

03.06.09   I studied for Sunday School lesson and for Precepts several hours this morning. I had a nice afternoon hiking with Betty. I talked to her about my taking Prozac or something to help me be more calm, and not so impatient with John. She takes several meds, so she was positive about it. I told her that I think I will put out a fleece, i.e., try to go two weeks without losing my cool, and go from there. I do not want to take meds for this trial; I want to learn what God is trying to teach me. I am re-reading Elizabeth Prentiss' *Stepping Heavenward*; it is so encouraging to know that there is another Christian who struggles with temper, patience, etc.

Meds, meds!

03.08.09   Almost lost it yesterday, but was able to control
my tongue and my impatience. We had an enjoyable time working
in the yard in the morning, and sitting on the back porch in the
afternoon. It was a beautiful day! Roger came up for hamburgers
in the evening. Today was lovely, too. Church service was inspir-
ing and the lesson from Isaiah 6 was great. We had lunch on the
porch, then went for a hike at Horseshoe park near our house. I am
looking for a hiking trail around here; one was to have been cut last
year connecting several of the state parks.

John seems to be getting along fine (when he is not trying to talk)
but tonight, he asked me how many of us were going next month.

I told him I did not know what he was talking about, but he could not tell me. Then he was confused trying to take a shower. He gets the shower and his closet mixed up, trying to take clothes into the shower to put away, or walking around naked looking for the shower.

Tom called yesterday, and suggested that he meet John and me in town some day, and he will take John to lunch and to visit the sick, or go somewhere. What a blessing that would be! So we plan to do that Thursday.

03.11.09   John got up this morning at 3:30 and got dressed, and ready for Awana. He walked back and forth in the house and finally came back to bed, but kept getting up and walking back and forth. I awakened but did not say anything; I was so tired, I just wanted to sleep! I stayed awake to make sure he got back into bed, and he did, but got up several times walking through the house again and again. He did not seem to remember any of it when he got up.

Midmorning, he asked me to come to our bedroom, he wanted to ask me a question. So I did; he looked all around in the bedroom, then in our bath, then went into his closet. He waved his hand around at the shelves, and clothes, and asked if he had to share this space with him. I asked who is "him"? He said, I don't know his name. I reminded him that only he and I live here; it is his closet,

and he does not have to share it with anyone else. I realized that
he might have been seeing his reflection in the mirror, and often
thought it was another person.

Yesterday we were in the bathroom at the same time, and he asked,
"What is your name?" I looked up at him, and he was looking in
the mirror.

03.12.09   Today was a truly bright spot in both our lives! He
and Tom did go out while I was in Precepts. They visited a man
in our church who has Alzheimer's, and has not been to church
in awhile. He used to drive the bus for the Awana kids. I had met
Ginger for lunch, and Tom and John came in to the cafe about
12:30, and told us about the visit. John had prayed with them, and
witnessed to them! The wife was there during the prayer, and she
told them she had never heard such a wonderful prayer. Thank
you, God!

03.13.09   I am not superstitious, but after a horrible night
and morning, I noticed the date... Not much sleep last night! I
forgot to take the sleeping pill I had planned to take. John was up
and down all night long. First he was coughing with a dry hack-
ing cough; we both were up looking for cough syrup (had none) or
cough drops. He took one, and it seemed to help with the coughing but not with the up and down all night. He kept going into the
bathroom, into his closet, etc. and back to bed, all the rest of the

night. I told him this morning, I need my sleep, so will sleep in the
guest bedroom tonight. He hates that, but I am sorry.

It was one little thing after the other after we got up at 6:30; his
pacing drives me crazy. It is as if he is looking for something, but
when I ask, he can't answer me. I do not know if he is looking for
something, or just nervous energy. I wish he would use the elliptical machine!

I found myself getting more and more impatient with his lack of
response to my questions, and with his walking all around the
house. I finally blew up, and even swore at him. James: "From the
same mouth come blessing and cursing. My brothers, these things
ought not to be so." Then I felt like I was going to have a heart
attack or aneurism (sharp headache) and was devastated with
myself. The "fleece" is over; now I have to ask for a prescription
for a Prozac-type med. I had tried to go two weeks without blowing up, to see if I could stay calm with the help of the Holy Spirit,
and I failed. John seems to be the one needing Prozac, maybe that
would calm him down from all that pacing. But he already takes a
med for that—Clonazepam.

I had made waffles for us for breakfast, but neither of us enjoyed them, with the tension hanging in the air. When we began our devotional time, I really did not feel like it, but knew I
needed it. When I started praying, I started crying, and so did

John. Praise God for his loving-kindness and mercies for us even when we do not deserve them.

We talked some after our prayers, and I asked him if he thought he could remember that when I was in a room studying with the doors closed, he could leave me alone. He said yes (but he doesn't) and apologized. I wonder if these incidences are God's way of telling me that it is time to stop teaching. To be honest, I'd much rather study and teach than be his caregiver, but that doesn't seem like God's plan for me right now. I don't know if I have mentioned the obsessive compulsiveness of this disease. He gets something in his head, and will *not* let go of it. Today it is a gallon of liquid that is used in boat toilets to keep odor out, not at all against EPA standards. I have told him time and time again that we can just throw it away, into the dump with other garbage. He is obsessed with disposing of it, as if it is a dangerous liquid. Sometimes I just want to scream! Even though he has sold all of his large woodworking equipment, there is still enough small hardware in the basement to open a hardware store. So we have already spent several days down there, organizing, and selecting what to keep and what to give/throw away. He mostly just follows me around, and does not remember what most of it is for.

5:30 PM; email to Betty:

This has to have been the worst day of our time with this dementia. I prayed for forgiveness for my mean-spiritedness, and my temper this morning, but John has absolutely "stepped on my last nerve" all day long. Not his fault! I found three of his pills on the table this morning, meaning he did not take his Aricept nor Namenda nor Clonazepam last night. He has been lost all day, wandering even outside the house, not knowing where he is nor what he is doing! I have asked him for forgiveness, as he has of me. God help us. He did not know how to get in the house from the garage, he put his shoes in the car, then was rambling about not driving, not knowing if we need gas, not knowing where the shower is, nor his closet. I walked him to the shower, and he kept coming out of the room "to take a shower." I finally walked in there and stayed until he undressed, and is now in the shower. Hopefully, he will remember to turn off the water, and get dressed! I feel like I should stay in the room with him tonight, to be sure he doesn't wander in the night, but I know that part of my problem is not getting the sleep I need.

I went into the bathroom to get him to come in for dinner when Roger got here. He was standing in front of the mirror just staring at himself. I asked him what he was doing, and he said, Just standing here waiting to see where I am supposed to go next..... I told him to come on in for dinner; Roger is here, and went back into the kitchen. No John..... Went back to get him, and he was still just standing in the bathroom...I guided him into the living room. He tried to say several things during dinner, but it was just confusion. He did pray the blessing, but jumbled it up toward the end.

03.13.09 Reply from Betty:

Anne, I am so sorry—

This condition seems to run two steps ahead of you. Now you have to watch him take his meds to make sure he has them - I will begin praying for your wisdom for the next step you may need to take—for both your and John's safety.

Reading other people's testimonials of how they dealt with something can sometimes make us feel inadequate if we don't seem up to whatever standard they managed. You have to look at how both of you are living.

It is not a sign of weakness—or lack of faith in God—to have John in a safe place where there are nurses who give meds on a given basis, who log what's been given, etc. You are not a nurse; you are a wife, a woman, a person who has basic needs that include regular sleep and the feeling of safety. You have neither now.

Your home should be a haven; not a place where you feel as if you're going crazy.

Homes are not safe places for people who have no idea where they are or what they're doing. Nursing homes have special alarms and can place sensor bracelets on patients so they don't wander off. Even the shower facilities are safer. Residents are guided to safe showers daily.

Anne, I know your immediate and church family church family would support any decision you make. Why don't you talk to Larry or your pastor and seek their advice if you are hesitant for this next step. This does not sound as if it is going to improve; you need professional help.

Anne, I was exhausted with Bob even though he was mentally clear most of the time; the intense stuff lasted for only about 7 months, but it took me most of a year to get my feeling of health back.

Please don't do this to yourself. I love you and am praying for you right now.

Your friend who understands warts and screaming and cry-ing and just plain feeling bad, love,

Betty

03.15.09　　　　Went to the annual Women's Spring Conference at our church yesterday. The speaker was Roseanne Coleman, and the subject was "Tell your story"—appropriately, since I am getting all this down in writing! I do pray that I can tell *our* story and help other caregivers who may go through this terrible disease with a spouse or loved one.

I make all kinds of promises about how I will be better, and how I will handle this going forward. Seems I do ok for awhile, then fall apart. My goal is to just keep my mouth shut! I find that when John is trying to tell me something, and can't, I keep questioning him, and get more and more impatient with him. Then he gets more agitated, and rarely can finish what he is saying. He always thinks he is somewhere else in the evenings; not sure if this is the "sun-downer" syndrome, or what. He asks if he can shave, or if he can shower, but never knows where the bathroom is, or his closet. I have to almost hold his hand after 7 PM. Betty came out this afternoon, and we had a nice visit. John was in the living room with us the whole time, did not talk much, but was pleasant. I have asked him to please not kiss my friends; that I would not like any man kissing me. A hug is fine, but no kissing. He says ok, but not sure he will remember it.

I am so much more relaxed and content when I am calm with him; I feel so wretched when I get upset with him. If only I could be calm all the time, and not expect more of him than he is able.

03.16.09   Today was going along well; we were doing the seasonal change in our closets. I had to do most of his; he was confused, but praise God, I was pleasant. He spent over an hour in the bathroom, and when I went to check on him, he was poring over all his razor blades, mixing them all up. He has several different razors, which take their own kind of razors, and it was a mess. I organized them once, he messed them up again, and I organized them again, and hid some so he couldn't mess them up again. All this time, I was able to be patient. Then after dinner, and after we showered, he got really weird. It was almost 8 PM, and he got completely dressed again as if he were going out. I saw him putting money in his sock, and asked where his wallet was, explaining that he did not need money, nor his shoes on, this late at night. He told me his wallet was at the office. He looked in the mirror, and asked his reflection if he could shed any light on this. He had talked to himself in the mirror as he was getting out of the shower, and even called his reflection "Mark". I hear him in the bathroom talking to himself often; just now he is in the living room, watching TV and talking to himself. Or maybe to the TV?

We looked for his wallet, and he kept insisting it was in his office (Norfolk Southern) and I reminded him that he had retired 9 years ago, and that office was in Ohio, not here. It got worse as we tried to talk, and I ended up crying and almost yelling. Oh God, please help me! Why do I think he can think and reason?!

03.17.09   Another rough day; why can I not learn his limitations?! After a terrible morning, and his telling me I acted like a "Dick Tracy," i.e., detective always watching what he was up to (I guess) , and me getting mad at him for not knowing I am trying to protect him and our home, I was so glad to have to leave the house and go to Renovaré. I stopped by the Free Clinic to see Karon; she was a God-send for my day. She talked about taking care of myself; I know I need to, but I also feel God has given me John to care for right now, and I want more than anything to obey Him (even if I don't act like I do!) She also brought up nursing home and finances. I had told John I was thinking of nursing home, and he pleaded with me to let him stay here. I prefer his being at home, but if I cannot get control of my temper, I need to do something! Karon suggested I talk to a lawyer about Virginia laws concerning Medicare/Medicaid, and moving some assets out of his name. We do have long-term nursing home care insurance, but it is only for 4 years, and only $100/day.

03.18.09   John got up at 9 AM this morning, getting dressed, and had me come into his closet to see his clothes all over the shelves. I reminded him that this was his closet, and that is where they belong. He had thought we were not home, I guess. He went back to sleep; I lay there for two hours, unable to go back to sleep. I have just tried to be quiet this morning, and speak only when necessary. He asked me, "Are you going with us this morning? I don't know who he thought I was, but this happens often. Ginger called with a Psalm she was reading in her morning devotions, and thought of me, Psalm 18; I so appreciate my friends who are mindful of my need of God!

03.19.09   This has been a good day for us. I led the last lesson in Revelation Part 3 this morning, and came home after stopping by the bank. We had lunch and then went outside to work in the garden. We planted a fig tree in the back yard. Then we worked on putting the fence up around the garden. I planted some onions; saw some deer tracks in the garden, so that reinforces the need for a fence! He "worked" in the bathroom and closet again for a couple of hours, messing up the organized drawers in his vanity. Oh well, if he likes it that way, I will leave it alone. His closet is getting disorganized again, but I will let it go too. As long as he can find his clothes...

I finished reading *Uncle Tom's Cabin*, and it makes me see what is just *not* important!

03.18.09   I have been working in the garden for a couple of hours, and just came in to fix lunch. I found John in the bathroom again, and I guess he has been there for the whole time I was outside. He has now taken all of his things out of the vanity drawers, strewn them all over the top of the vanity, and when I walked in, he was using the mirror to try to "fix" his razor, i.e., pressing the metal end of it against the glass. I told him that could scratch the glass, to please stop. He told me he knew I had organized everything there, and someone came in and messed it all up!

03.22.09   The last two days had been ok; he is obsessive about his toiletries, and about packing for the trip. I helped him pack and told him not to open the suitcase again since everything is neatly packed, and he has duplicates of the toiletries. I thought he had left it alone. He was restless in bed last night, so about 10:15, I went into the other room to sleep. I slept ok, but about 5:30 I heard him walking around the house, going out for the paper (never comes until 7 on Sundays), so I stepped out and asked him to please take off his shoes if he were going to be walking around. He didn't. Finally I just got up about 6:15. When I went into our bath, I saw a shoe on the edge of the tub with a toothbrush, toothpaste and deodorant in it. (?)

This moving stuff around drives me up the wall; then he asks me to find whatever he lost by misplacing it.

At lunch he asked me if I knew where his (made motion of shaving) was. I told him it was where we left it yesterday: in his vanity top drawer. He did not say anything, but a few minutes later, I saw him digging though his suitcase to get it. (He has an extra one in there). I just flew apart, and screamed terrible things at him, for not doing what I asked him to do, i.e., not unpacking, not taking so many jeans (he had put more clothes in it), leaving his razors, etc. alone. He kept standing there saying "I'm sorry" and it was all I could do to keep from slapping his face! I was so angry. I know that we need a sedative for either him to settle him down, or for me. Now I feel absolutely wretched and just wish I could die. 9 PM: all is well, or at least ok for now. I realized later that he had forgotten everything that had happened today. He once again did not know we were at home. I had to actually *take* him to the bathroom, he could not find it, and then practically *put* him to bed. This is moving way too fast!

Thinking of nursing homes

03.28.09   We had a nice trip to Williamsburg March 23–27. Sally and the kids got there about an hour after we did, and we had a nice condo at Wyndham Governor's Green. (our timeshare) We spent the first two days in Colonial Wmsburg, and the last day at old Jamestown. The weather turned out colder than we thought, but Nigel was sweet and let me wear his jacket! John enjoyed being with "his family," and was quieter than usual. He lagged behind us most of the time; Sally or I would drop back to walk with him. He only got lost from us once, and it scared him. He tried better to keep up after that! I have realized how obsessed he is with his clothes and toiletries, not sure why. We got back home about 3:30

on Friday; he tried to call his mom, but can no longer remember her number, nor does he remember how to use a phone.

He is so confused when we get back from a trip, but he seems to enjoy being with me/us on the trip, I guess it is worth it. As we were getting closer to our house on the way home, he asked me if I planned to stay "with us" when we got home. He continually thinks I am another person.

I went into the bathroom to check on him, since he had been in there an hour, and he was in his closet, shaving! dripping shave cream all over his bench and the floor! I nicely directed him to the sink. I had cleaned the toilet, and asked him not to go in that one if he needed to use the bathroom, so I guess he thought that meant the sink, too.

He got up twice last night in the middle of the night, and got dressed. I had to tell him both times to take off his jeans and shoes, and go back to bed. He did not remember any of this when he got up.

He drove me crazy with the packing for the trip. I do not plan to tell him about our May trip until the day before we go!

03.29.09   Yesterday afternoon and evening were difficult; he kept wanting to ask questions or talk, but nothing was making sense. Roger came up for dinner, so he and I talked, and John interjected occasionally. He got up in the night to go to the bathroom a couple of times, and I always wake up, and listen to be sure that is what he is doing, and that he gets back into bed. Once early this morning, I heard him get out of bed, but felt so groggy, I was not fully awake. Then I heard tinkling *not* in the toilet, and jumped up. He was in the living room, and had peed on the floor! I asked what was he doing, and he said, peeing. I got him back to bed, and spent the next 15 minutes cleaning up the hardwood floor. Thank goodness it was not on the rug.

I am tired. 8 PM: it has been a much calmer day than last Sunday, thank God. If I can just remember to zip my lip! He asked me this afternoon if I did not like him; I think it was because I have been so quiet today. He has spent hours in our bathroom and his closet; going through things, looking at his Awana materials, etc. When I went in there this evening, he was talking to himself in the mirror, and it occurred to me that that may be why he stays in there so long: talking to himself, although he thinks it is someone else. He is so restless; I need to ask the doc if there is something that could help his restlessness.

I keep thinking about putting him in a nursing home, usually when I am upset with him. Then I want to cry to think of him being there and me here at home without him. Today was my last Sunday for teaching the class of ladies; the teacher will be back next week. I will miss them, but I will be glad not to have to be doing the intensive study for teaching. I think John needs me with him in our couples' class. Still not sure what God wants me to do about the summer Bible study...

03.31.09   But I do know that I am *not* pleasing Him with my anger and impatience with John! He got up about 3:30 this morning and got dressed to go outside. I told him (patiently!) that it was middle of the night; to come back to bed. He did, but then was restless and got up about four times to go to the bathroom. Of course, I had to lie awake to be sure he was using the toilet! Mid-morning, I went into the bathroom, and he had my vanity drawer open and was putting things in it. I lost it. I have asked him over and over to not go into my vanity, that maybe I should put a lock on it. He insists he won't do it again, but I am sure he does not remember that. I went downstairs to use the elliptical machine for 20 minutes, and when I came up, he had taken all his clothes off the rods in the closet and piled them up on the bed, along with all his shoes! I (stupidly) asked him what was he doing, and as usual, his response was "What am I doing!?" and told me he had been fired. "The man" is coming to get his things. He had been watching TV, and I guess he imposed the actions on himself. Now he is in there, hanging them all back up. and I am sitting here shaking like a leaf in anger, at him, and at myself for my lack of self-control. I did call the nursing home and found out it is $149/day there; our policy is $100/day for 4 years. Oh God, please help me!

5:00 PM: We were only three of us for Renovaré today, but I was so thankful we met! I can bare my real self, sins and all, to them, and pray with them. When I got home, John wanted to shower and shave, so I went into the bathroom with him. (He pays no attention to the DO NOT ENTER sign I had put on the door) As I stood back, watching him shave, and trying to prompt him for the question he had been trying to ask me for half an hour, he began talking to himself in the mirror, again thinking it was someone else. He asked, "Where do you work? NS railroad? I thought so. What is your name?" He never waited long for a response, but kept talking to "him" about our house and our floors being wooden, and couldn't put water on them. I am not sure if he was thinking about peeing on the floor, or about the North Dakota floods that are on the news. I finally asked if he knew who he was talking to, and he said he was not sure of his name, maybe Monk or Mark or something. I asked if he was familiar with mirrors and reflections, and he said yes, but did not connect it with his talking to the mirror. I finally got him going on shaving, and left to get dinner ready for our company. Wayland and Gale are coming for dinner tonight, so they can get to know John better, and perhaps come stay with him sometime to give me a break. I talked to Betty briefly, and she is going to call Woody, our long term nursing home insurance agent, for me. I will be at Betty's tomorrow, so I hope to be able to talk to Woody about what our policy covers when John is so physically competent, but mentally undone.

04.01.09   Nice dinner with friends; John talked more than usual, but did not make a lot of sense. They were so attentive and sweet to him, and Wayland offered to take John for coffee, or visiting, etc. whenever I want to bring him into town with me. So we have planned for the three Thursdays of the April study, to meet up with him.

Betty called later, she was able to catch up with Woody—good news! Our policy is lifetime, not just 4 years, and the value per day is now almost $140. I hope to learn more today.

Last night was a nightmare all night long. We went to bed at 10:00, but neither of us could go to sleep. We both tossed and turned for awhile. John got up about ten times in just a couple of hours, wanting his shoes and pants, to "leave." I had to get up every time, because he kept opening drawers, moving things around, etc. About 2, he got dressed, and went out the back door from the bedroom. I stayed up, and heard the garage door open (how in the world can he remember that code!) so went to let him back in the house through that door. He went back to bed, but not to sleep. I think I got about two hours of sleep, and am shaky and exhausted, and angry. When he got up about 6:15, he went right to the mirror and started talking to his friend in the mirror... I had prayed last night that God would give me a sign if it is ok to put him in a nursing home; was this it? This morning, he came into the kitchen, and said, "Good morning!" and I responded, "Bad morning!" He asked

why, and I told him it was because it was a bad night... he did not
remember any of it.

04.02.09   Went in to Roanoke, took his mom to lunch and
grocery shopping. He was so confused trying to get her groceries
into our car. I left him with her at her apartment and went to our
CPA to pick up our tax documents, then on to visit with Betty for
awhile. She always has a nice dessert and coffee for me to enjoy!
She is really pushing me to put John in a nursing home, I guess she
is thinking of my health and well-being. But I realized I probably
use her as a sounding board, and she thinks this is worse than it
really is. I did call our insurance agent, and the company, to get the
ball rolling just in case. He and I went out for dinner before going
to church, and he could not eat all his meal—symptoms like
acid reflux.

After we got to church, and I was in prayer meeting, the Awana
leader came to get me, to come see about him. Same symptoms, dry
heaves and feeling awful. A doctor at church checked him out and
thinks it is acid reflux, too. I brought him home and he went right
to bed. We got several phone calls asking how he was. Our church
family has really rallied around us! Many prayers lifted during
prayer meeting. We did sleep better last night; both of us were
exhausted. I think our throat, esophagus, sternum pain is plain old
stress! This morning has been better; I feel calmer today. I talked
to Sally about the nursing home option. She and Susan had talked

yesterday; they both are ok with whatever I decide, but seem to feel this is too fast. It will be interesting to see what Susan thinks after getting home next week from being gone six weeks! He has spent hours in his closet today, moving his clothes around. I just caught him taking two dress shirts outside, and asked him where was he taking them. He responded that he was taking them to the car, so he would have them for this weekend. I talked him into putting them back in his closet, and he did. A few minutes later, he came by here with two suits on hangers, same reasoning. Again, I (calmly, believe it or not!) told him to take them back to his closet; this is his home, and his closet, and they will be here for Sunday. He went back that way, but in another few minutes, here he comes again with the suits, heading toward the garage end of the house. I just sent him back to his closet again, and told him to come back to the living room, and leave his clothes alone in the closet. Our friend Gale called and offered to have a list of in-home helpers sent to us, in case I need someone to stay here at night, or during the day so I can get out. I think we have enough friends who have offered that I don't need more help, but it will be nice to have that handy, just in case.

04.06.09   I have not written in a few days because, praise God, life has been going relatively smoothly for us. We have been able to sleep better, although he always gets up once or twice (or more) to go to the bathroom, and goes the wrong direction, and I have to re-direct him. Then it is hard for me to get back to sleep; he

doesn't ever remember it the next morning. Last night was rough;
I don't think I got more than four or five broken hours of sleep. We
worked in the yard and garden Thursday, Friday, and Saturday. He
is willing to help, but has a hard time following directions. Roger
came up and used the John Deere tractor; we both explained to
John that he should not be operating it. John used the self-pro-
pelled mower and did ok, but missed areas. Roger went over those,
so it looks nice. John ran over the newly planted fig tree; not sure if
it will make it now. John and I raked up the cut grass and wheel-
barrowed it to the compost pile. He seemed lost at church, but still
ushered. I am so thankful to the men who help him continue that
job. I have been having second thoughts about nursing home, but
will continue to pursue it, just to be ready if and when the time
comes.

A note from Ewans' life: Nigel got smacked up side of his face
(accidently) at a home-school function and passed out. Had to be
taken to the emergency room, and had CT scan; seems ok now.
Thank God Chip found a forum for caregivers of LBD patients that
I joined. It will be helpful, I am sure.

And from Roger:

> Just talked to Sue and she's excited that it's less than 48 hours
> before we're on the road. Looks like it might be rainy Monday
> night here. We might want to get on the road towards Raleigh

shortly after 6 just to make sure we've got plenty of time. Once she's home, we can talk about whether there are things that we can do to help with John like having him down here some days to give you some rest time.

Time for a nursing home?

04.06.09   5:00 PM: We met Gary at Dairy Queen at 11:30;
left John with him and went into Rocky Mount. I went to Trinity
Mission first, and had a nice visit with Eddy; turns out he is Donnie
and Marie's nephew! He gave me a tour of the facility; it is very
nice. Some of the residents make you want to cry, but the facility
itself is ok. I was shaking like a leaf in a storm as I went in; Eddy
said, "Sit down and take a deep breath!" I asked if it was that obvi-
ous, and he said yes. I almost cried a couple of times, thinking of
John being there, and me at home. Eddy answered all my questions,
and gave me some literature to peruse. I left there and went by the
Free Clinic to let Karon know what I was doing. It is like going to a
counselor to be with her; she is so comforting, and loving. She was

very supportive, and is like Betty, in that she is encouraging me not to wait long to do this. I am glad some others, like Brenda and Sally, are more reluctant to see this take place. I need a balance. I do not want to "push" him away and feel guilty, nor do I want to keep him home and feel proud. I continue to pray for wisdom and guidance from God.

I mailed the POA to AF&L (the insurance company), so I can deal directly with them, and John will not have to. I received from them the paperwork necessary to get insurance coverage when the time comes. (If)

Next step is to make a doc appointment—another blessing: our doc is one of those for Trinity! John likes Dr. A; that will make it a little easier. Eddy said to let Dr. A know I am pursuing this path.

Not sure if I will check out the other home; I have heard from a number of people at the church, and Karon, that Trinity is the better place.

04.08.09   Had a good night's sleep last night! I moved the furniture so he could not go outside through the French doors, and closed the bedroom door, after turning on the night light in the bathroom. The cover over the mirror in our bedroom seems to help with him knowing which way is the bathroom in the night; it was reflecting the bathroom before. I slept in the guest bedroom

went to bed at 9 PM, and woke up a little after 9 AM! Thank God!
I plan to continue this. He has been ok today, although he often
comes in to where I am, and asks me to come with him to another
room, he has a question. Usually the closet or bathroom (seems
to be obsessive about those rooms) and his questions never make
sense. I worked in the flower garden for several hours today; he
was inside most of the time. We are taking care of the animals for
a few days, until Susan and Roger get back from Phoenix. He gets
confused just taking hay over to the fence for them. I had taken
a shower, and he was getting ready to take one, when I saw him
standing in his closet, naked, staring at himself in the mirror. I
left him alone for awhile, then asked what was he doing. He was
absolutely fixated on his mirror image, for about 15 minutes. It was
creepy. I finally got him into the shower and away from the mirror.
I have called and made an appointment with our doc, to ask him
about Prozac for either/both of us.

04.10.09 Listening to the news, I realize how focused I have
been on our situation here at home, even with our country going
to hell, or to socialism and hyperinflation. But I can do something
about our situation, nothing about our state of the union! It has
been a rather easy last couple of days; I have been able to stay calm.
We worked in the yard Thursday, and that was nice. I did not sleep
well last night, watching for Susan and Roger to get home. I knew
it would be after midnight, but it was almost 4 am when I heard
the dogs barking wildly, and looked out to see the horse trailer

tail lights going down their driveway. I had been praying off and on for their safety getting home, and was thanking God for their being home at last. Susan came up and visited for a little while this afternoon; it was *so* good to see her! She told me about her 6 weeks in Phoenix, the work there, and the time with friends, and horse lessons. She enjoyed it, but is glad to be home. Roger will have to go to Washington, DC for a week in Apr and 3 weeks in May. I could tell she was not happy about my thinking of taking meds for my stress; in fact, she and Sally think John should go off his meds and just see how he does without them. I plan to talk to Dr. A about this when I see him next week. After a couple of days like these, it is hard to believe I was thinking about nursing home for him.

04.12.09   Another pretty good day. I went down to Susan's this morning, and she invited me in for a cup of tea. After about an hour, I came back up the driveway, and into the garage, where John was. He was ok, just said he missed me. Not sure he knew where I was... The creepiest thing he is doing these days is his talking in the mirror to his reflection; he truly seems to think it is someone else. Also his taking his clothes on a hanger from his closet toward the garage. I usually stop him and tell him to just leave them in the closet until he wants to wear them. He still is confused about this being our home.

04.13.09   Beautiful Easter: seems that I received a new blessing about the meaning of the resurrection this year. I have believed in the crucifixion and resurrection since I was a child, and have thanked God so many times for Jesus dying for me, and the gift of eternal life through Him. But this year was especially poignant for some reason; thinking of Jesus coming out of that tomb, alive forevermore, as a "first fruits" for us, was so uplifting. It is hard to put feelings into words, I just thank God for this faith.

Nancy came up Saturday to Cheri's, and they picked up Mother at Richfield, and Louise at her apt., and drove out here for a late lunch/dinner. Rafael came separately since he had to leave later for work. Susan and Roger came up, too, so we had 9 for our Easter dinner. It was nice, but so sad to see Mother so mentally gone. She did not really know most of us, nor where she was. But thank God, she is pleasant and sweet. Louise was patient with her, although Louise talked constantly as usual, and got on everyone's nerves. If only she could learn to *listen* to others, too! She fell right on her butt, going out the door to leave. We got her up again, and she seemed ok.

We missed Joyce; she called on their way to Karen's. She talked to Mother, but I don't think Mother knew who she was.

I am getting good sleep now that I am in the other bedroom, but I miss my own bed. As far as I know, he is not getting out of the bedroom. Last night, I left the room normal, no furniture moving, but still closed the door to the hallway. I wonder if the sleeping is what is helping me stay calmer with him. I have stopped getting so upset when he doesn't "mind me." Maybe I am finally learning his limitations!? My neck is really bothering me again; I guess it is stress. I was studying the lesson for Thursday's Bible study, and he interrupted me to ask a question about postage. Interruptions get my mind off-track; that is why I am not sure I should try to teach. When I get upset with his interrupting me, it breaks my bond with him, and with the Lord.

Email from my cousin Linda:

My Precious Anne,

I love you. My heart aches for you and John. How could you bear up under this stress without our Heavenly Father and those he places in your pathway to encourage and support you? Dear cousin, please know that I am praying for your physical and mental health, so that you can make the right decision about John's care. Please know that I am praying for you daily and that I will ask our Sunday School Class to join with us in prayer. You actually should send your musings to a publisher. Your words are as poignant as the books I read about Alzheimer's. There but for the grace of God go I. Ross and I get so frustrated when we can't find things or manage all the activities we are doing. We know nothing about what you're enduring. Even with Mother, we could at least take breathers when she was in the nursing home. I am thankful that we don't know what we'll be facing down the road.

"Sufficient to the day is the evil thereof."

Thank you for sharing your innermost thoughts, Anne. I can't tell you how much that meant to me. Please write often. You will always find a heartfelt, listening ear here.

May God continue to grant you wisdom to make the decisions he would have you do.

With love and deep empathy,

Linda

04.16.09   I left John alone at home to go to Renovaré Tuesday; he seemed to do fine. It was raining, so he did not go outside. Wednesday he and I went in to Roanoke to take his mother to grocery store; I took lunch for us to her apartment After taking her and John back to the apartment, I visited with Betty for a couple of hours, before going to church in the evening. I can relax at Betty's, and it is a good break for me. This morning, he went in to church with me; I had Bible study and a doctor appointment He and Waylon visited with Way's brother Bill, who worked for NS when John did. The doc appointment was interesting; it was really for both John and me! I asked Dr. A about stopping the Namenda, which I had recently learned seems to make delusions worse. He was not in favor, so I won't. I asked him about my taking Prozac or something similar, to help me with my impatience. He was not in favor of that, either, which surprised me. He does not think I need it, that I just need to recognize my own limitations, and not

be so hard on myself. He said this stress I am under is the worse
kind, i.e., caring for a dementia patient. I told him about my chest
pains, and was having them while there. He ordered an EKG, which
showed nothing different from the last one a year ago, but is having
me go to Roanoke Memorial to have echostress tests on Monday.
Gale called this evening, and said John talked a lot, and made
sense, except when he lost his train of thought. They again offered
to do anything we need them to do.

04.17.09   We enjoyed working in the yard today; he is willing
to do whatever I can practically stand over him and instruct him
to do. It is worth it, though, because he enjoys being outside and
working. I lost my cool after we came in this afternoon. I was sitting outside on the porch reading, and he tapped on the window for
me to come inside. When I did, he led me (for the hundred time)
into the bathroom, asking again which sink/vanity should he use.
I had come in earlier and he was shaving over my sink, and I directed him to his own. He had put toothpaste ON his razor. I took out
his shaving cream for him to use. I am not sure why I get so upset
with him for moving things around on the vanity tops; I need to
not care! We both apologized to each other, and the evening has
been fine.

We had two couples from church over last evening for dinner, and
had an enjoyable time. John joined in the fellowship, had trouble
finishing his thoughts most of the time he tried to converse, and

after they left, he said, "I want to be in the group, all these people going through here, and I want to be your friend." Of course, it took him a while to say all that, and I am not sure I understood what was going on in his mind.

Update on our day (April 20) in hospitals: The stress test was a "walking nuclear stress test" and took 3½ hours! I won't know results until later this week, but I am sure my heart is fine. The doc and technician for the treadmill part said they had patients half my age who couldn't do it like I did. Two women from our church were there with us; I was glad for John's sake, since we had thought it would only take one hour.

Then he had an appointment this afternoon, which has turned into two more doc visits. (It is no fun getting old!) He goes to a podiatrist tomorrow afternoon to have that callus cut out of his foot, and then a urologist appointment is next week. I am exhausted, and I am sure he is, too! Louise had an appointment Thursday afternoon, but was kind enough to cancel it. (She just called me back and asked me to call and cancel it for her.)

Email to my cousin Linda:

> Hi beautiful cousin,
>
>   I was thanking God this morning, for allowing this hardship in my life to bring me closer to you! He always gives us

silver linings!

The doc who told me he did not think I needed meds like Prozac is also John's doc. When we were there yesterday, he gave me some samples of a med (Seroquel) to help John rest better. John wants me back in our bed, but I cannot sleep with him, because he is up and down so often in the night, and I wake up and cannot go back to sleep. I have been sleeping a good eight hours a night in the guest room, and feel so much better. Maybe with John sleeping more, I can have some down time myself. I was able to get up at 6 this morning, and get some Bible study done before he got up!

Love,

Anne

04.27.09   I got a call from Dr. A today: my heart is normal, just fine. That is all he said, so I do not have any "next steps" planned. I will just learn to live with the stress?

Foot surgery

John is having the foot surgery Thursday morning; we did the pre-op lab tests last Thursday. Things have gone pretty well for awhile, but today was another rough day. We worked in the yard, and he is just so confused, and unable to follow instructions. His "helping" in the yard causes me more work, although he still can push the mower, he has a hard time starting it, filling the gas tank, staying off rocks and even ran it into a pile of limbs. That pulled out the fuel line, and it took me awhile (he was lost) to figure out how to fix it. I don't think the new med is doing any good. I try to be quiet when I get up in the mornings, but it is not long before he gets up, too. I had hoped for some quiet time alone.

04.30.09   Today was John's surgery; we got to the hospital

at 7:15 AM. I had asked our former pastor if he could meet me

there, to have some time to talk. I wanted to talk with him about

my off and on feelings of putting John in a nursing home. He was

very attentive and asked good questions. I got teary several times,

especially when I told him about my inability to control my temper

with John. Our new, young pastor came in after a few minutes, and

mostly listened to us, rather than adding any thoughts of his own.

I had talked to him some time ago about my Bible study teaching,

and whether I should continue, but the nursing home discussion

was new to him. I had not talked to him about that, since I seem to

be going on a roller coaster about it. It seems that the times I am

strongest about the idea is when I am least patient, so that led me

to realize I was not ready. When things are going well with us, I do

not want to do it. Selfishly, I do think about having time to do what

I want to do, if I did not have him to care for. Then I remember

the Scripture about unselfishness and service to others, and also

about those wedding vows: in sickness and in health. Larry said

from what I was telling him today, he does not think it is time; in

another 4 months (I told him I would not do anything before end

of summer) we may be having a different discussion. I got John

home, but in the 8 hours since we got home, I think I have told him

25 times, "Put your foot up." He is supposed to keep it elevated for

the next week, and stay off it for the next few days. He just forgets.

I want to be patient with him, and not badger him, but after a while, it gets to me.

John was pretty alert and making sense before surgery. Even after the surgery, he was doing well. We got home and had lunch, then sat in the living room, watching TV. I had to keep reminding him to keep his foot propped up; he forgot every three minutes. Unless I had ice on it, he would put in down. I told his at about the 35th time, when I get to 50 I may scream! He also kept getting up and walking, which he is not supposed to do. I noted a couple of times, his orthopedic shoe was on the wrong foot, and he was walking on his bandages, a no-no.

This kept up until about 8 PM, when he went into the bathroom. I went in there, and he was unwrapping the bandages. I stopped him, and rewrapped it, telling him again that they have to stay on until next Thursday. About 8:30, I went in to see about him, and he was doing it again. I told him to leave the bandages alone, and go on to bed. In a few minutes I went in to take his pills to him, and he had stripped off all the bandages, and got back in bed, bloody sheets and all. I hit the ceiling, lost my temper, etc. *Ugh*. I hate myself when I lose control like that.

05.01.09 I am a little (very little) better this morning. I did not sleep well at all—too churned up. At 4, I got up to go to the bathroom, and noticed that the master bath light was on. I was so tired, I just ignored it, and went back to bed. Did not sleep again, but got up about 7:15. I made coffee and read the paper, listening for John. I heard noises, and voices (friend in the mirror?) about 8 or so, so I went in. He was up and dressed, with a dark sock over his foot. He had again taken my bandaging off, and put more on himself (I saw the empty box). I told him (took three times) to take off the dark sock; put a white one on.

I called the doc's office, and we went right in. I told them what was going on, and the doctor kindly scolded John and tried to impress on him the importance of keeping the bandages on and elevating the foot. John was so agreeable, and told doc he did not even remember taking those off last night. I told doc that John could not remember for more than a couple of minutes. The doc re-bandaged it, checked the incision, pronounced it ok. He knows Karon from the Free Clinic, who had offered to come here if John needed his bandages changed. So he gave me a handful of gauze bandages and ace bandage, in case I need her to come, if John does the same trick.

I cried on the way home, I am so exhausted. I feel better now. Sally called, and Suzanne, and Louise. I finally just handed John the phone after Louise had talked and talked and talked. She kept saying, He does fine when he is here! I finally said, Maybe he should come live with you, then! He does not do fine here. She called back a couple of times, with "advice." I was able to be nice to her; I know she means well. I worked in the yard, John sat on the porch watching me, with his foot propped up.

Susan and Roger came for a little while this afternoon, and Roger brought me a couple loads of horse manure. They came for dinner tonight, and that was nice.

05.06.09   Had quite a time with our smoke alarm system over the weekend. After not sleeping well Thursday night, we were awakened about 5 or 6 times during the night Friday night, with the smoke alarm going on and off. Tom and Debi came over Saturday to clean the alarms out; they stayed for tea and left about 3 PM. Ten minutes later, all of the alarms came on and stayed on. I called a neighbor who had installed our generator, and he came over. He found the faulty one - in our bedroom - and said to get it replaced. He would not take any pay; a nice man!

We went to church Sunday. John sat next to me in church for the first time in ages; he is usually ushering and gone most of the service. He had a chair to put his foot up on for church service and for Sunday school; that was the longest he has had his foot up since the surgery! He has to be told over and over to put it up. He keeps putting the orthopedic shoe on his good foot.

Roger came up to get the lawn mower ready for Susan or me to mow while he is gone to DC. Then Betty came for the afternoon.

John seems way out in the twilight zone. He has not complained of pain, so I only gave him one pain pill this morning, no more today. I wonder if the pain pill is making him more loopy. The new med does not seem to be doing anything. I cancelled our May 17–22 trip, since we don't know how his foot will be then.

05.04.09   Today was a good day for working in the yard; kinda cloudy, but little rain. So I worked outside most of the day. Susan came by in the afternoon, we had iced tea on the porch. She offered to come with a book and sit with John half a day a week, so I asked her about Tuesdays, so I can continue in Renováré. Her offering to do that lifted a huge burden from me! I felt "free" on Tuesday, with Waylon coming and getting John, knowing too, that Susan will be here other Tuesdays. To Roanoke on Wednesday, leaving him at Louise's and getting to see Betty or Cheri (or Mother?), and then the men at church who are willing to come. So my spirits were lifted.... until middle of the night last night: I heard noises at 2 AM, garage door opening, footfalls in the hallway. I knew it was John, but still scary. He was fully dressed, jacket and all, carrying several shoes, and looking vacant. I just directed him back to the bedroom, told him it was 2 AM, to go back to bed, and slammed the door shut. Then I could not go back to sleep. I tossed and turned for about 4 hours, and finally fell asleep, when I heard him in the hallway again, lugging something. It was the bench from his closet; he said he was taking it down to the music room. I said "sewing room"? He did not know. He did not remember anything from the

2 AM incident. I lost my temper *again*. The chapter from our Sunday School lesson was too appropriate—about our heart and our tongue. It hit hard. I apologized to him, but I am truly exhausted, and worn out from all this. I seem to pray for forgiveness every other day, and ask God's help daily, hourly. Where are You, God?

05.07.09 Better days are always ahead if I could just learn to be patient. Wednesday visits turned out well; Betty always makes me feel rested, even if I had not slept well the night before! We went to the Awana dinner at church; he got pretty restless, but was OK. I slept better, but had trouble falling asleep. Got up at 11 to take a sleeping pill, and slept until 7:30 this morning. The weather cleared somewhat, a beautiful day, so I was able to work outside for several hours before going to the doc to see about his foot healing. Doc changed the bandages, but told him he still must stay off it for another week. He was obedient to that order for about 10% of the time last week! So when we got home, I put a big orange bow on it, and told him to remember to keep his foot up! He looked like a present!

My friend Lucy sent this message to me, in response to my sending her part of this journal:

> You need to invite all of those people, Pastors, children and friends to come take care of your husband for four days while you go away and then they will get the picture. I hate to be so

blunt, but Anne you are killing yourself. Who do you think is going to take care of all the details in the nursing home if you end up in the hospital? The first rule is take care of yourself and you are not doing that. I doubt if your pastors have had much first hand experience with people with dementia. It is easy for your children and the pastors to give advice. They are not living with it day to day as you are. Please do not be offended by this letter but my heart bleeds for you and you don't have the benefit of a good support group with counselors who have been there like I did. I hated putting Bob in a facility, but I knew it was the best thing to do for my own sanity. Once he was there, then I could let them do the nitty gritty stuff and I could enjoy being with him because they live for the moment. You can let your pastor and your kids read this letter if you want to.

Remember, you cannot reason with a person with Lewy Body or any other dementia and they are not logical.

Fondly,

Lucy

05.09.09   The past two days have been ok; he is so confused about this being our home. He asked me last night if I was ready to leave. I asked him to go where, and he responded, Home! I told him we were home, and he did not say more. Today, he asked me twice where could he sleep tonight. He whispers as if he doesn't want someone to hear him. He spoke to the empty chair next to him at lunch. The bow on his foot seems to help him remember to keep his foot up, but I still have to remind him often. I am enjoying working in the yard; created a new flower garden, and worked on the bare spots in the lawn. He has to be practically led from one room to the other; it is like he either doesn't understand, or doesn't know the house.

Joyce called last night; I had sent her Lucy's email. I can't tell what my sisters or my daughters are thinking about a facility. I know Nancy (and Joyce and Cheri probably) think I should go on something like Prozac, and I might be able to deal with this better. They may be right. I plan to call doc on Monday, and try to get something for either John or for me! I don't really want to place him in a facility; I would really miss him. Even though he is not all here, not the man he used to be. But he is sweet, and good company most of the time!

05.11.09   I realized that I should write more often when things are going well. We have had a good few days, even though he is not remembering to keep that foot raised! I had prayed Sunday morning for God's strength and love, needing the Holy Spirit to help me get through the day with Louise, Mother and John. I had asked Him a few days ago if He was there to please let me know. Well, He did; He was with me all day long. Thank you, God. Even as I would begin to feel impatient, I remembered that I had given this day over to Him, to serve Him, by serving our mothers. So the day went well; took Louise to her church, the same one that we had started out our married life in. Then to lunch, then the three of us went to visit Mother. I was glad Louise went with us; Mother is hard to have conversations with, but Louise talks freely to anyone! Mother was SO happy to see us; I was so glad we went. I was tired by the time we got home, but thanking God for a good day in Him.

It rained all day today, so I got some "inside" work done. John sat watching TV most of the day; spent his normal hour or more in the bathroom and his closet. He asked me this morning "Where have all the boys gone?" I asked him who was he talking about, and he did not know. Yesterday, he blamed Mark, his "friend" in the mirror, for taking his watch. It was in a drawer. Brenda and I talked and prayed this afternoon over the phone; I am so thankful for that time with her. Also for Betty, and my Renovaré friends, my other church friends, my sisters, and my daughters and sons-in-law. When we have days like these, it is hard to think that at other times I am ready to put him in a facility. I pray this continues!

05.14.09   It did not continue past Wed morning, but praise God (and John) for being so forgiving. I woke up in the early morning to go to the bathroom, and could tell by the lights reflecting outside the windows that John was up. I went back to bed, and when we met later in the kitchen, he started talking about "we were moving furniture around." I asked where and we went back to the bathroom and closet. He had taken everything movable and rearranged them all over the place, and was blaming "those boys" for doing it. I lost my cool, put everything back where it belongs, and then felt terrible. We had our devotions as usual, but not before I apologized to him and to God. The rest of the day went ok, I spent most of the day in the yard, mowing and moving mulch. One of his friends came by in the afternoon for a short visit. I will be glad when the doc releases him so we can work outside together. He will be able to mow and to wheelbarrow mulch! We went out for dinner, to Lowe's for some plants, and to prayer meeting at church. He was enthusiastically welcomed at both prayer times; the Awana is over for the summer. He even prayed in both; only God knew what he was saying, but you could feel his love for God in his words.

We went back to the foot doc today, but he was out on emergency, so all they did was re-bandage it. We go back to have stitches removed next week. He was told to keep it elevated another week; it looked kinda swollen at the stitches. I am so tired of telling him over and over to keep off of it. I am so tired of this 24 hour job! He really is lost in the house; always going the wrong direction, forgetting what "closet," "shower", "garage" , "dirty clothes" mean. He undresses in the kitchen or living room before taking a shower. I have to direct him to his closet, then to the shower. I sent part of this journal to Sally, in response to an email asking how we are doing, and here is what I got back:

> Hi there! I wondered if your lack of extraneous comments when sending your journal entry was an indication of fragility. I have

had a very difficult week myself. I can't wait to see Jesus face to face! I'm sorry for the commotion Dad caused.

I just want you to know that I will support you in whatever you decide to do, whenever you decide to do it. I am praying for strength, compassion, patience, wisdom, and discernment for you.

I love you!
    Sally

My response:

It was really because I wanted to get outside before it starts raining! I am ok, although I am weary of these "incidents"!

I was outside, and he came out and told me we need to get to the doctor; someone called from "Dr. Winslow's" office and asked if he could come in for our "missed appointment." He told them we could come right away (it was 12:15 and I was sweaty and dirty.) We have an appt. with his foot doc at 2:00. I assumed he meant Dr. Wiznant, the urologist whose appt. we missed when he had foot surgery.

So I started calling to cancel; after 3 phone calls, it turns out it was Dr. Clements (foot) office, asking if he could come in at 2:30 instead of 2:00. I was ready to kill him. But I kept my patience, with difficulty. I have continued to have to say over and over for two weeks now: "Sit down and keep your foot up!"

Thank you for your prayers; those characteristics are exactly what I need for this! Every time I think of his being in a facility, I get sick to my stomach. That is not what I want, at least not now. But I do appreciate your support.

I love you more,

Mom

I had made chicken salad and dropped by Ginger's to give it to them, but she was not at home. She broke her foot Saturday, so may have been at doc again. So we had it for dinner! I was able to work outside again after we got home; it seems I want to be outside all the time now!

05.15.09 Spent most of today outside, working along the fence, digging out the grass so I don't have to use the weed-eater there! I am trying to make the yard more mower-friendly, without having to use the small mower or the weed-eater. Susan is so good to keep the lawn mowed, or Roger when he is here! John stayed inside most of the day, hopefully keeping his foot elevated! Sally called this afternoon, and while we were talking, Susan came up. How blessed we are with these two wonderful girls! They talked to each other while I made iced coffees for Susan and me. I talked to Susan about John and his condition; she has been amazed at how much he has gone down since she got home from Phoenix. She knew when she got home that he had regressed, but even more in the four weeks she has been back. I told her I wanted to be sure she and Sally were with me, when the time comes for facility care. She knew Sally had said she was OK, and told me she was just concerned about me living here alone. I told her I was not scared to be alone, but I knew I would miss him terribly. He came outside with us a couple of times as we were visiting, and asked questions that did not make sense, so she knows he is "not with us" mentally. I told her I hoped to make it through the summer with him. I had to guide him through getting ready to shower; he was really confused with getting undressed, and getting into the shower. so sad...

It is 2 AM and I heard his footsteps in the house. I lay there for a little while, hoping he would go back to bed. I saw lights go on and off, and got up to see what was going on. I went into the bedroom, and he was dressed and walking around. The sheets were torn off the bed, and everything in the bathroom that was movable had been moved—a mess in there. I yelled at him to get back into bed, and he just looked at me as if I were crazy. He did get back in bed, but not before grabbing my arm and jerking me; it still hurts like a burn. I guess that means he is capable of "violence" of some sort, and I should do something. I had a hard time getting back to sleep, needless to say.

Now it is 9:15; Gary is coming over to sit with John so I can get some things done. We were up this morning, and it seemed he had forgotten the 2 AM event. Susan was coming up to have waffles with us, and as she was coming in the back door, I noticed she was talking to someone: John was coming in behind her, having gone out the front door without my notice. He had a pile of clothes in his arms, and was asking her if he boarded here (home), could he come work for her—he had been fired. She reminded him he had retired years ago, and he seemed relieved. Then she noticed that he had regular shoes on: he had taken his bandages off his foot, and put on regular shoes! So she tended the waffle maker while I re-dressed the foot. I am tired and weary. We had planned to go to Margie and Gary's to dig more flowers, but I called and told Margie we would not be coming. That is when Gary called and offered to come out.

Nancy sent me an email about a documentary on Alzheimer's; she thinks John has this instead of Lewy Body. I just talked to her on the phone, and she was so comforting. She is encouraging about his going into a facility.

Advice from friends

05.18.09   A wonderful message from Pastor Stan yesterday on anger. I really have an issue with anger, and need to learn self-control. I prayed for help from the Holy Spirit, and was able to just be *quiet* yesterday, and we had a nice day. Betty sent me a harsh email that surprised me, since her friend BK had hurt her by trying to tell her what she should do about a man she met. I will print it for "posterity":

> This is Betty "butt-in" - something like the advice Betha K. is planning to give me about re-marriage even tho she hasn't "been there, done that"

Anne -

I said I wouldn't say anything again, but you're my dearest friend and I have to make an observation -

initially, your plan was "whenever he becomes incontinent"; next was "not before Easter; maybe after Easter"; then "maybe after his foot heals"; and now "maybe by the end of the summer." Each of these "deadlines" has occurred after some horrendous action taken place.

Anne, once you move into "hating" and telling him that, how much more do you think you can take?

If you were telling me that you are handling this emotionally and otherwise, I would not say anything. It seems to me that you're waiting for a quorum (maybe with Larry's ok) before you make the decision.

Yesterday John misinterpreted your action of removing his glasses and twisted your wrist - all of us, animals included, do not let anyone near their faces unless they totally trust someone. That would indicate that John is past the mental capacity to know he trusts you.

I love you and I don't want to see you messed up emotionally or otherwise. This is sad, very sad, and that's not going to change.

It's not as if you were in the time of Moses and you took the person out to the desert to die. John would be going to a facility where there is someone there, awake, 24 hrs a day. You've said that, if he were in a facility, you would probably see him only once a week. Even if you saw him every other day, at least you would have several days of a little peace.

Being mentally ill, as you already know, is totally different than physical illness. My mother and brother were both mentally ill, God has certainly helped me recover, but I assure you, Mother is the reason Portsmouth has such horrible memories for me and why I don't want to return.

I know you want to honor God through this. At the same time, God has placed people in your life to give you advice, hopefully not like Job's friends!

Love, Betty

I did not respond to her; we can talk about this later in person or on the phone. Sometimes email can betray emotions. And then, three days later, she emailed again:

Anne -

I'm sorry I was so out of line and hurt you deeply.

For the past several months, I had been thinking about your friend in Renovare who had said she thought you had accepted John's illness on one level but not on the other. And you were appreciative of her calling that to your attention. I remember sitting there thinking, "I've thought the same thing for a couple months but I didn't think you would want me to say anything about it since I had come down so hard initially at lunch one day begging you to take John to a doctor for evaluation."

My main concern is for your emotional and physical safety. I know without a doubt that your first concern is to do God's will. I also am ashamed of myself for jumping over that line.

I realize that this has probably caused you not to share any more with me about your feelings, your pain, your anguish. I will pray that the Holy Spirit will help me hold my tongue and let me be available if you decide to do that again. If not me, please find someone you can share that with so it's not bottled up inside. I've learned that journaling helps, but not the way that having someone close listen to your heart's cry.

The amazing thing is that I have let my tongue be my rudder after two weeks of Ed's preaching on the danger of the tongue, pride and humility (lack thereof).

This is the second time in a week that I have or have probably screwed up big time with two people important to me by saying far more than I needed to. or should have. Definitely not the tongue's fault, but that of my heart and pride.

I love you. I could tell in your voice last night that I had hurt you, and I couldn't think of anything to say at the time.

Betty "Biden"

My response:

> Well, I was more surprised than hurt, in light of your comments about BK's comments to you about dating.
>
> I don't remember your "begging... evaluation." —I remember you telling me that Bob said I needed to get John to a doc, and I did shortly after that.
>
> You are very astute, Betty; yes, I did decide that I should stop telling you everything he did that upset me. Your picture of our life was based on the times I was upset and angry. But I will not stop; I do need you to listen -- key word: listen. :)
>
> I can relate to your comments about holding your tongue; after Stan's message on anger Sunday, I determined to be more self-controlled. It lasted all day Sunday. :)
>
> I will pray for you to have control over your tongue, and to think before speaking. I need the same prayer from you for me.
>
> I love you, too! Anne

I had asked Lucy for her thoughts, after sending her some journal entries, and here is that correspondence:

> I am going to copy the newest entries in my journal for you to read. I think it is time, and I now have both daughters on my team. I have been sending Sally some of the entries so she can see the day to day stuff, and Susan has been spending more

time with us, so she is seeing it first hand. My sister Nancy
told me about watching HBO's series on Alzheimer's (Nancy's
husband had Lewy Body, but was pretty docile, so he stayed at
home until he died of a heart attack.) and she thinks John has
Alzheimer's, not LBD. She is also encouraging about a facility for
John. Let me know what you think, and didn't you tell me not to
try to prepare John for this, but just to take him there?

from Lucy:

Yes, I think it is past time before you have a nervous break down.
Remember the first rule is take care of yourself so that you can
take care of all of the business of having him in a facility. I think
he has Alzheimer's also. He is acting like my friends' husbands
who had Alzheimer's. He may have both. They can go together.
Bob was originally diagnosed with Alzheimer's by the U WA well-
ness clinic where he was in the clinical trials. The LBD, was discovered in the autopsy but the autopsy said that he most likely
(about 80% sure) had Alzheimer's also. You have an awful lot on
your plate with taking care of a yard and everything. I am glad
that your daughters are on board with you. In the Alzheimer's
conferences I went to they always told us that the patient will go
along on a plain and then take a definite drop. It sounds to me
that is what is happening to John. If you have a facility get him
on a waiting list right away because a lot of places don't always
have a bed for Alzheimer's patients. Good luck and keep me

posted as to your decision. I have you in my prayers. Ask your
daughter to quit praying for patience because Joyce once said
to me that when we pray for patience God sends us tribulation. I
always asked my friends to pray for peace, guidance, strength
and provision.

Love,

    Lucy

Am I only recording the difficult times? Am I only telling Betty
the worst of this? Do I need to be sure to record the days that are
calm and even enjoyable? I feel so often that I just want to be free
of responsibility and go when and where I want to go. But is that
what God wants for me? Does He want me to be totally devoted
to this task at hand? and learn from Him? I just do not know, but
until I am *sure* beyond question, I cannot take this next step. I
worked outside today, but not before calling the doc and asking
him for a prescription for John's Flomax, and if he would prescribe
a low dose of Prozac for me. He did, so I will pick it up tomorrow,
and hope it helps me stay calmer. John came outside several times:
once to ask me if he could go home; once to tell me the pharmacy
had called and I needed to call them (it was the doc's office, not the
pharmacy); and once to ask me if he could have my permission to
call for a helicopter. Each of these questions took about ten minutes each to ask, and the last was really to go 30 miles from here to
take a shower! I talked to Nancy and to Cheri, and will be meeting

them at Cheri's on Wednesday. They both are relieved I am
getting Prozac.

Here is Lucy's latest email:

> Maybe it is Satan and not God who is causing you to be so inde-
> cisive. In the long run it might be better for John to put him in a
> facility. Once he is used to it (and I have it on experience from
> a nurse who used to be in charge of an Alzheimer's unit that it
> doesn't take them more than about 3 days) he won't have so
> many things to move around and so many rooms to wander to.
> Once they start wandering away from you it is really not safe for
> them and you can't be on guard every minute of the day. While
> you are outside sometime he could turn on a burner and burn
> himself or the water and forget and flood the place. Think about
> it. When he is as confused as you say there are too many awful
> scenarios that could happen. He would be safer in a good facility.
> Just a thought anyway.
>
> Fondly,
>   Lucy

05.20.09   Yesterday was an emotional day for me; lots of
thinking to do. I still have not talked to Betty, and every time I
start to pick up the phone, something stops me. Maybe my venting
to her is unhealthy for mine and John's relationship, and God is

telling me to stop. I will call her soon, but will tell her right away
that I don't want to discuss the situation with John with her. I do
not want to lose her friendship.

Monday was a tiring day; I got a lot done outside; John pretty much
stayed inside, hopefully keeping his foot up. I noticed this morning
that it is swollen some. He came outside several times to ask me
questions, but had a difficult time articulating; i.e., after stumbling
with words for several minutes: I need a helicopter to take me
about 30 miles to take a shower. Not in those exact words, but that
was the message. Then the doc's office called, but he took the message like it was the pharmacy. So I spent about 15 minutes trying to
find out who called and why. We had a quiet evening, but he got up
about 10:15 PM and was opening the door from the kitchen to the
porch. I got him back in bed; he was blaming "those kids."

I cleaned house Tuesday morning before leaving for Renovaré. I
stopped by the pharmacy to pick up my Prozac (yes, I broke down
and got it), and then by the nursing home to talk to one of the people in charge, Sherry. One problem with Trinity is that they have
no special facility for dementia patients who need one-on-one care,
or who might go outside. I don't know how long John will not need
that. I stopped by Free Clinic to see Karon for a few minutes; she,
Lucy and Betty are strongly "encouraging" me to move ahead with
the nursing facility. I did set the wheels in motion but told Sherry
I may not do it for awhile. I continue to ask God to give me clear

direction. I just hope I recognize His "voice" when it comes. Susan stayed with John for me to run errands and go to Renovaré, and when I got home, I asked her if she thought it had been necessary for her to be here. She just shrugged. She told me not to send her any more emails from Lucy; she was kinda angry that any one who doesn't know him is trying to tell me what to do. She was rather abrupt, and I got teary. She assured me she would be supportive of what ever decision I made, but she wanted it to be MY decision. I told her it would be. I fretted over that for awhile, but remembered Stan's message on anger, and got over it! Our devotional study was on humility this morning. As John was reading it aloud, I remembered that I had been praying for years for humility, after my self-centeredness in my career days, and the lesson was teaching that service to others brings humility. God, is that You speaking? I just helped him get his shower (just have to wrap his foot in plastic, and direct him to the shower.). Now it is my turn!

05.23.09   Still have not talked to Betty, but have exchanged emails. We are OK. She has asked for advice on how she is handling her latest eHarmony connection.

Twice a year, we help Susan and Roger with the gathering of hay bales, along with the Holley family, who has all the equipment and gets half the "crop." John stayed in the house Thursday afternoon; we had just had his stitches removed. He got into so many things, but did not cause any damage. I find things moved from room to

room, and in cabinets and drawers they don't belong in. So I had
him ride with me (I am the truck driver!) going through the fields
as the others loaded up the bales. We worked from 11 until 6:30
Friday; a beautiful day. Roger came up for breakfast waffles this
morning; Susan left for horse event in Lexington Friday morning.
John has been easier to live with the past couple of days; is it the
fluoxetene? I have been on it for four days now.

05.24.09   John and I went to Lexington to see Susan in the
cross country event; it was a nice trip, about two hours each way,
a beautiful day. She seemed glad we had come. On the way home,
John asked me if I had a daughter who worked for the railroad.
I asked him if he knew who I was; no response. He later asked
another personal question, and I again asked if he knew who I am;
he finally said, Anne. Roger came up for dinner, and we enjoyed
his company. John seemed really confused about where he was in
the evening; I had to help him get his shower, get ready for bed, and
get into bed. I did not sleep well; was continually listening for him
to get up (he didn't). He ushered at church this morning, thanks
to his usher friends! Went out to lunch with Tom and Kristen; he
did not have a lot to say, but it was a nice time with them. Pleasant
afternoon, on the porch reading. Some thoughts: I have not talked
to Betty in almost two weeks; just emailing. Wondering if my
impatience with John has anything to do with my not being able to
spend time with my best friend, and resenting it. I re-read the book
on relationships and Jesus, and was convicted anew that John is

my priority, and if I were truly humble and loving, he would be my focus.

05.27.09   I do wish I could get over the resentment of having to go in to Roanoke every week and run Louise around. I am thankful for her friend Norma, who will take her to doc, or grocery every now and then. This fluoxetene med makes me sick to my stomach, and dry mouth, so I really don't feel very well. gripe, gripe, gripe... *stop it*!

I am not sure the med is making any difference in my patience level with John, but at least I have not lost my temper in a few days! We had a nice Memorial Day—quiet. Susan and Roger, and Betty, came for BBQ and Betty and I were able to have a nice visit sitting on the porch in the afternoon. Susan came up yesterday to stay with John while I went to my Renovaré meeting. I love those women in our group; I thank God for them. I have been able to do a little yard work, in between the other activities. John even got out and raked some. We have had lots of good rain lately. Sally called and asked about them coming here July 11–14; hooray! I miss them! It will be interesting to see what they think about John; she has not seen him since March in Williamsburg.

06.02.09   I was just telling Nancy this morning that I thought the prozac was helping—ha. I didn't really lose my temper, but I surely was angry. I cannot understand how he can seem to be ok with some friends, and cannot put a sentence together that is understandable around me. He and Waylon went golfing this morning, and they seemed to have had a good time. I did not get a chance to talk to Waylon to see how John was. It was nice to have several hours alone in the house. I organized (for the 100th time) his closet, even took out some of the not-worn shirts, to make more room on the shelves and hangers. After he took a shower, he took down five shirts/shorts/jeans to wear! I had him put all but what he wants to wear back on the hangars/shelves, and asked the *why* question. I should learn not to ask why; it only escalates into my anger and his inability to talk. He kept trying to ask me something; I was patient for about half an hour. But then the hundreds of words which did not make sense turned into what sounded like an accusation of another man in my life. He did that once before, and it drives me crazy; I do not know what he is thinking. I called the nursing home this morning, to let them know maybe early August would be the timing of his admittance. After this evening, I am ready! But I do not want it to be this way...

06.04.09   We had a good day Wednesday (June 3): went over to Gary and Margie's to dig up plants to bring back here. My memory garden for Grace is full of plants and flowers from her gardens! We ate at DQ on the way home, and I was able to get some of the plants in the ground before the storm hit. I am reading *Sarum*—a history of England, by Edward Rutherfurd, and enjoying it; great reading for relaxing afternoons.

We stayed home and prayed here last night; after a busy day, I did not want to drive back in to Rocky Mount to church. I have pondered Vickie's comments at Renovaré Tuesday: she kindly and lovingly told me that my personality had changed in the last few weeks (prozac? or weariness?) She said, "We have almost lost John already; we do not want to lose you, too. You have lost that sparkle in your eyes." Sally had just told me over the phone that morning that I had sounded very tired the last few times she has talked to me. I decided this morning to stop taking the prozac anyway; it makes me so nauseous, as well as dry mouth and jittery. I feel fine today. We worked outside all morning, planting, and weeding, and picking peas. John watches me more than helps me, but if that makes him feel more a part of "us," that is fine. I did talk to Betty for a little while; she is getting ready to go on vacation next week, so it will be awhile before I talk to her again. After we came in and ate, then showered, I noticed that he was trying to push his towel into the mirror for his reflection (Mark?) to take, he kept at it awhile, then just started staring into the mirror with a goofy grin on his face. I have gone back there several times in the last half hour, but he is still there, almost catatonic. I am leaving him alone; not sure whether to "wake" him up or not.

06.07.09   A pretty good weekend. I continue to try my best to understand John's comments and questions, but it is so difficult. He just does not make sense 90% of the time. Today is our 45th wedding anniversary; he is not the same person (I guess I am not, either!) that I married, but I do love him. I see him often standing in front of the mirror, and can tell that he thinks he is talking to another person. He has started blaming "him" or "them" for crazy things he does.

06.12.09 I feel so agitated myself today; was awaked at midnight with John walking around the house; had to take him back to the bedroom and into bed. I did go back to sleep easier than usual, maybe because I was calmer with him than usual! This morning, he is into everything; picking things up and moving them, "measuring" things in the bathroom. I have been trying to study to teach Sunday School on Sunday; we are in Galatians 2–3. I am having a hard time concentrating, maybe because of being impatient with him? He is in the bathroom now, taking the night light in and out. When I asked him what he was doing, he said, "Trying to learn more about electronics." ... "about locomotives." I do wonder if it is time for the nursing home, just so he is around people and doing activities with others. He just wanders around here, unless we are outside and he can do yard work with me. My assignment for Renovaré this week is to write a letter to God, and I want to do it about John's condition:

> Heavenly Father,
>
> I am so confused and unhappy today. After being awakened again at midnight (it has been awhile, I must admit) by John wandering around the house, I got up grumpy and impatient

with him. He did not remember it, as usual, and asked what was wrong. I reminded him of how frustrated I get when I lose sleep. (Not an excuse for impatience, I know!) We had a pretty good day yesterday, working outside in the morning, and just taking it easy in the afternoon. We sat outside in the evening, and watched a storm come in. He has been going to bed by 8:30 or 9:00 most nights. I have been trying to prepare the lesson for Sunday every day this week, and I get side-tracked, and it is hard to concentrate. Not sure if that is because of him, or just me being out of sorts. I keep checking on where he is and what he is into. I find that when I am most ready to admit him to a facility, is when I am upset and impatient with him. Although lately I have thought about it more when I see him wandering around, as if he is looking for something or someone. He was so used to being busy all the time when he was well, and now he just wanders around. Susan told me that she gets so antsy with him on Tuesday afternoons because of his restlessness and wandering. Maybe it is good that she is here with him, to see how he behaves. It would be interesting to know what she and Sally are talking about as they have these few days together in Columbus this week. I pray that they will honor You with their conversation, and be more able to help me with this decision. I want to honor You, as well, with this decision. I pray for Your wisdom and guidance, Lord. Help me, I pray. Often, when I hear Stan preach or read a passage from Scripture, I feel that I am supposed to just give my self to his care, keep him here at home. So many friends say, "You will know when the time comes..." Since I *don't* know, I guess "the time" has not come!

06.14.09   I talked to Sally this afternoon; from her comments, I don't think she feels the time is right. She told me she asked Susan if she thought that he was at a point to be institutionalized early August. Susan told her she had not heard that timing from me, and did not know. They both have given me encouragement that whatever I decide will be ok with them, but I surely do wish I could hear one of them say, "It is time, Mom." I noticed this afternoon that he comes outside where I am every time I get on the phone, but goes inside when I am just reading. I guess he wants to hear what I am saying to people, as well as wanting some "social interaction." That also makes me think he would be happier at Trinity, where there are people all around, and activities he can do. We enjoyed last night's Sunday School class party at the lake; good friends, and good food, and we were able to go out on the lake in their pontoon. That was so nice; made me miss living on the lake. Of course, we would not be taking boats out! Lucy emailed me that she is sending her diary of when Bob had dementia, so I can see what it was like for her, and perhaps may help me.

2:30 AM Monday morning: I thought I heard a noise, so I got up and could see the lights were on in our bedroom. I went in there and he was dressed, and had taken everything out of his closet, and hung it on the towel bars in the bathroom, or laid it on the floor or vanity tops. Also had moved the few things left in the bathroom all over the place. He seemed unaware of anything, except to try to get hangers undone from each other. I asked what he was doing and he said trying to do something good. I got him back in the bed, and left the mess. It will be interesting to see what he thinks when he gets up in the morning... I am all jittery; hope I can go back to sleep.

10:00 AM I finally went back to sleep, and got up around 7:15. I read the Bible awhile, to keep me calm, and then went into the bedroom. It looked like a tornado had gone through; worse than at 2:30 am! He was standing in the middle of the mess, looking puzzled. He said it was that boy who was there. I left him there to start picking up, and he worked for about an hour alone, getting nothing done. He kept picking up shirts, and bringing them into the kitchen. After about the fifth time with the same shirts, I asked if he had a problem. He said he could not find the closet, so I walked back with him and pointed it out. He hung those up, but kept coming back into the kitchen with other clothes. He finally had breakfast, and I went back with him to help. We got it done by 10, and I am exhausted. I took a bunch of winter clothes that had been in storage boxes back to the basement. He had stuffed lots of clothes that had been on shelves and hanging up into the drawers of the vanities. I do not know what causes this kind of activity, but I praise God that I was able to stay calm and just get it cleaned up. These are the kind of things that make me more comfortable putting him into a home!

It seems that he is needing me more and more for simple things, like finding the bed at night, getting ready for bed, reminding him to brush his teeth, and watching to be sure he puts toothpaste , not shave cream, on the brush, not on a razor! He puts his toiletries in the oddest places. I have to find his things for him often. He sometimes needs help finding the shower, knowing what to wear, etc.

06.17.09 and now he needs help finding the bathroom! Lucy sent me a diary she had kept while Bob was suffering from this, and it is like reading my own journal—so many symptoms the same. He started forgetting how to use the bathroom. He saw people who were not there. He did not know his home was his own. John asked me today how was he going to get home. I pointed to the house (we were outside) and said that is our home. He was puzzled. Later, he commented on how nice my yard and gardens look—still believing this was not his home.

06.18.09 I drove us to see Nancy today; six hours in the car coming and going; he was very quiet on the trip and at her house. He evidently forgot we had gone as soon as we got home: he told Roger we had gone off to take care of some business. He was pretty confused this evening; he came in the kitchen talking about measuring the cabinet tops, and said something about Pennsylvania. I was talking to Betty on the phone, and he came out on the porch, with the razor in his hand, shaving his face. This was the saddest/ hardest bedtime yet: He kept trying to tell me why he had the razor in his hand, but could not explain the problem. I asked him if he could show me, so we went to the bathroom. He opened the drawer where he is supposed to keep his razor, combs, toothbrush and toothpaste. He took out a comb, and it had shave cream on it. I had just washed all his combs yesterday.

Then he took out his toothbrush, but we could not find his tooth-paste. I finally found it with his deodorant in his tennis shoe in the closet. He thanked me and was able to brush his teeth. Then he went to the bathroom, and I noticed him talking to "Mark" in the mirror when he came out. He went into his closet and I asked him what he was doing. He said, I am going to bed; I told him to come out of the closet, his bed was not in there. He tried to get up on the sink vanity as if it were a bed! I guided him to his bed, and kissed him goodnight. I have noticed that when I say good night, he doesn't answer, he just looks sad. He has lost more weight, even his legs show it. He looks good anyway; still a handsome man.

Needing to be helpful

06.21.09   Father's Day. Sally called, and he talked to her for
a few minutes, very slowly and haltingly. Susan and Roger had us
down for dinner this evening, and he was ready to come home in
an hour. He did not talk much, but ate well. The last few nights,
when I am helping him get ready for bed, he has said he wanted to
ask me something, and I wait while he tries for ten minutes or so.
He never can get out enough for me to even know the subject. We
kiss, and hold each other, and then he goes to bed, looking unhappy.
We worked in the yard yesterday, raking up piles of grass. He
works very slowly, and seems to have to stop and think about what
he is doing. I was trying to show him how to put the compost into

the wheelbarrow, and he would just take it out after I put it
in. Frustrating!

06.24.09   We enjoyed working in the yard this week; it is nice
to have some sunny weather! He wants so much to be helpful, and
I appreciate what he is able to do, but he needs constant direct-
ing. He forgets what he is doing, and then needs hands-on help. Oh
well, at least he *feels* helpful. I started a new Bible study yesterday
for five weeks; teaching I John. I dropped John off at Waylon's and
he and Way later came to church for the JOY club luncheon, while
Betty and I went to lunch and hiking. When I came home, John,
Susan and Roger were at the pool, so I changed and went down
there and cooled off—how nice! John and I are creating a new garden behind the house, and enjoying that work—at least, I am! Roger
came up with his tractor this morning and plowed it for us.

06.25.09   I painted a section of the fence today. John asked
me this morning if there was anything he could do besides paint. I
suggested he rake a part of the yard that had lots of thatch in it, so
he did. We had a nice lunch on the front porch, and then we worked
together in the new garden, digging out rocks! We went down to
Susan and Roger's and got in the pool for a while. He has been in
and out of the house since then: I have been reading on the back
porch, and he comes out for awhile, then goes back into the house,
roaming from his closet to the kitchen and back, over and over. He
came back out this evening as I was getting up to come inside, and

asked if he could ask me a question. (That usually ends up with his

not being able to articulate whatever is in his head.) So I listened

to him, and he said, "Since I have been in this place, I have not

felt like I belong here. I think I would like to go back to Roanoke,

and see what I can do in the church." Me: "Which church?" Him:

"Franklin Heights." Me: "That is in Rocky Mount. Where would

you live, and who would take care of you?" Him: "I don't know." We

went on like that for awhile, but I never really understood what he

was thinking. He is bored here, I know; he is so used to being busy.

We have kept busy on nice days, working outside, but evidently

that is not enough. I wondered if this conversation can be the door

opening for him to go to Trinity. We never reached a conclusion,

other than his agreeing with me that there probably is not a place

for him to live in Rocky Mount, nor any work at the church he can

do. He came into the computer room later, while I was typing this,

and thanked me for helping him. Then said, he just wanted to be

helpful; I reminded him of his help in the garden!

06.27.09   We worked in the yard most of yesterday; he even

used the small lawn mower. Left areas unmowed, but enjoyed the

work. We usually sit outside on the porch after we come in and

clean up. He always needs help with getting undressed, putting

his clothes in the hamper/basket, and finding the shower. I have

started putting his clean clothes out for him; he stays in the closet

for so long, just moving clothes around. We had planned to watch a

DVD, but the TV quit on us. Susan and Roger came up to see if they could figure out what was wrong. They brought a pie, so we enjoyed dessert with them. They stayed awhile, but could only surmise that something is wrong with the TV, not the dish or the DirecTV itself. I don't miss it, but he does. Today we went in to Roanoke, took a squash from the garden to his mother, and then went to see my mother for awhile. Had a nice quick visit with her. Then to Betty's, for a gourmet dinner! mmmmm... He has been quiet since coming home this afternoon, walking around a lot, in and out of the house. I have been on the porch reading, and he will sit with me for a few minutes, then he is back inside. He has asked a few questions that don't make sense. He came in and sat on the floor next to me at the computer; I asked what he was doing, and he said he was worried for me. He heard there was a judgement. I asked, "God's judgement?" and he said "That is what I want to find out."

06.28.09   He ushered today, and got confused, and almost went to the other side of the aisle. When we got home, he was talking about a "Mitch" taking pictures all around the house, to break in. Then he was talking about being watched while we were at Betty's; I think he saw our reflections in the mirror, and did not know us. He is hallucinating often now. I wonder if I look for reasons to admit him to Trinity. Sometimes when I think of being here in this house without him, I get sad, but so much of the time, I am just tired of trying to understand him telling me or asking me things, and especially tired of his pacing around bored. I think he would be happier where there are people and activities, since there is nothing he can do in the house any more. Since half the time he doesn't seem to know that he is in his own home, maybe it won't matter to him.

06.29.09   Another night of horrors... He went to bed about 8:30 PM; I went to bed about 9 PM. Tired from doing nothing? Awakened about 2 AM and got up to see him standing in the hallway door to the garage, with his laundry in his arms. Led him back to his bed, and noticed that everything was a mess (again) in the bathroom, and this morning, noticed the bed, nightstand and pillows on chair had been moved. He was dressed, so I directed him to take off his shoes and shorts, and get back in bed. I did not go back to sleep for several hours; that kind of awakening is so disturbing. He is very quiet this morning; but does not remember last night's episode...

7 PM: He just did something to the TV in the guest room, and we cannot get a picture. He just punches buttons. He has not said any-thing today that has made sense. We worked in the garden again; he works the ground where I have already been, and most of the time, I just let him dig away. He does haul the rocks into the woods for me; that is a help. I had to quit and sit down after lunch, and I called Cheri. While I was talking to her (on the porch) he came up and stood there staring at me. I asked him what he needed, and he said, "I have been charged..." so I asked him to wait and tell me after I was off the phone. Later, he had the mail in his hand, and

the newspaper was lying on the table on the porch, and he said, "it is 1.5%, I owe it, and it is because I touched a lady that I should not have..." I asked where had he heard that, and first he said, in the paper, and pointed to it, and then he said, on the news. I told him he was not important enough for that to have been in the paper or on the news, and that was not something he would do anyway—everyone loved him. He thanked me for believing him, and for saying that everyone loved him. I wondered later if he had read the articles about the SC governor, who had had an affair, and thought it was him. Brenda and I are talking/praying on Monday afternoons now, rather than Monday evenings, and he usually comes out on the porch while I am on the phone. I asked him to watch TV while I talked and prayed with her today, so he stayed in the house. He and I went down to Susan and Roger's for a swim later, and then back home for the evening. Susan showed us what looks like a bear print in the dirt near the barns. Eeek!

Preparing for admittance

06.30.09   The Prozac did not help this morning. After he went to bed last night, about 9 PM, I was in my bedroom talking to Joyce (sister) and he got up and starting rambling through the house. I got off the phone, and asked what was wrong: he couldn't sleep. I wanted to go to bed myself, and will not go to bed without him being in his bed, so I got him back to bed. and I put a big chair in front of his bedroom door. This morning about 5:45, I heard noises, and a huge crash. I looked out the window, and there he was walking down the porch steps and down the path, with only a shirt and under shorts on. I knocked on the window, and he came back toward the house. He had come out through the bedroom French doors, knocking over the grill that was barring the way out. It was

in pieces, and he was rambling on about trying to "save" me, that
he saw pictures of people with their heads in the toilet. I could not
make any sense of it; we picked up the pieces of the grill. I will try
to put it back together later. He has said several times already this
morning (7 AM) that he does not know where he is. I try to patiently tell him that he is at home, and the guy who "took pictures"
is a figment of his disease, not real. He looks lost, and confused. It
is heart breaking, but I am losing patience. I plan to go by Trinity
today, and see what needs to be done next for admittance.

9 PM: I dropped John off at the Scotts', and went to Trinity before
Bible study. I always get so nervous there; this is a tough decision!
Sherry was there, with a woman in her office, who turned out to
be the director of the facility. I talked to Sherry about timing, and
we settled on July 27 for admitting John. I was shaking like a leaf
by the time I got to the church; I asked a couple of the women to
be praying for me while I was leading the lesson. Betty said it went
fine; she couldn't tell that I was nervous. She and I had a quick
lunch, and then I went by the doc's office to set up the chest x-ray;
for July 10. After Renovaré, just Joyce S and me, I went back to
Trinity to spend some time with the director.

I was calmer in the visit that I had been this morning when I met
her. Betty had prayed for me at lunch, and Joyce at Renovaré, so I
settled down some. I still feel a little bit jittery, not sure if I am still
afraid this is not God's will, or just the doing of it. Marie and I had

a couple of minutes to talk after class, and she is very supportive. I asked Waylon how their day went today, and he was really positive about it; Gale said she could tell a difference from the last time, two weeks ago. She keeps encouraging me to get day time help, but that is not what I want. I want to be at home, without all this stress, even if it is without him. Since he doesn't seem to know this is home, I hope it will be an easy transition for him. or at least, not difficult.

I kept smelling something in our bathroom, and could not figure out what it was. I thought maybe a mouse had died in the walls. I burned a scented candle for several hours, but the smell was still strong. I went into his closet, and looked down into a trash can there: he had peed in the trash can—ugh!

07.01.09   We went in to Roanoke as usual today; I dropped him off at his mom's and visited with Betty for awhile. Then we took Louise to grocery, but did not have time for a meal with her. She takes so long grocery shopping, I think I will start getting her list from her over the phone and doing her shopping. We went to church this evening, and he was pretty quiet. After he went to bed, I called Sally (after sending to her and Susan the last few days of this journal, and the date of July 27.) I heard a loud banging and got off the phone to see what was going on. He was in the bathroom, banging on the mirror at his reflection, fighting the image with all his strength. There are marks all over the mirror where he was banging with his shoes; it is a wonder it is not broken. He is now back in bed, I pray he sleeps. It is 10:15, two hours later than his usual bed time. I am shaking all over.

07.02.09   He stayed in his bedroom the rest of last night; looked lost this morning. We went on a picnic on the Parkway with friends from church, and enjoyed the day; he was pretty quiet. Susan came up this afternoon and had iced tea with me on the porch; had a nice visit. We were finally able to talk about the situation without him around: he stayed in the house most of the time. She had not seen my email of last night, so the violent episodes were news to her. She told me how he acts when at their house on Tuesdays; it is sad and scary. She assured me that she feels it is time, and I told her how much that meant to me that she said that. She also agreed to go with me to admit him. I feel a weight off of my shoulders, having Susan's "approval" and agreement. He has gone to bed now (8:30) and hopefully will stay in bed all night.

Note from Sally:

> I just read your message about Dad banging on the mirror. Then I read a message from my friend Julie in GA, and I thought her words were good:

> "As hard as it will be for your mom to put your dad in a home, it will be the best thing! We were just at making that decision for

mom when she died. She should not feel guilty, as he will get the care he needs. And , honestly, he doesn't really know! She can be more loving and helpful to him when he's not her responsibility alone. It may sound harsh, but while we always *love* them, it can get hard to *like* them at times. And, yes, your mom will recover. But, it will be a long time before she can remember him like he used to be. It is only really happening for me now, and it's been 7 years. That's my perspective, anyway."

07.04.09   He did stay in bed the night of July 3, but got up at 2:00 AM last night, turned on lights all over the house, and when I came in to the bedroom to see what was going on, he was up and dressed and walking around. It took a few minutes to get him back in bed, and took me a couple of hours to get back to sleep. We had a nice July 4 celebration dinner at the Swartzes' last evening, and Betty was with us. John was quiet, and ready to come home too soon. We will work outside today, then go to a picnic with some church friends of Susan and Roger this evening.

5:20 PM: We worked outside most of today. He mowed, but cannot get the bag on and off anymore, so I had to do that part. He was taking the tools to the shed, but could not figure out how to close and lock the shed door. He has asked several times today about a class, but cannot explain what it is. First he said four-year-olds, then five; he had "seen" kids in the yard several times.

07.05.09   Had a nice time at Kenny and Sherry's last night. Susan and Roger had invited us to come to their church gathering; their interim pastor came, and we had a Bible study on the Lord's Prayer. It was thought-provoking. We went to bed shortly after returning home, and went to church this morning. He ushered, but got mixed up with the offering plates; no disasters, thanks to God. He fell asleep in Sunday School, on the way home, and after lunch, sitting at the table. The last was sad: his head was bowed down, and he was drooling. Then he napped all afternoon; not sure what that will mean for tonight's sleep!

He just came into this room, and said, "I am kinda miffed about something." I asked what, and he said "That bunch... [hesitation]... wants us to work in the nude." I asked what bunch, and ascertained it was himself in the mirror. I reminded him that that was him in the reflection, so he must have been thinking that. He stood here with his arms folded for a few minutes, and left.

07.08.09   Relatively quiet couple of days. He is going to bed earlier now; still gets up around 6 or 6:30. I go into my bedroom and read before going to bed, usually 9:30 or 10. Praise God we have had several good nights to sleep. We worked in the new garden again Monday; I transplanted some blueberry bushes into it, and planted some beans. He helps by hauling the rocks off for me. He used the trimmer, and did fine. He seems to forget what he is doing a lot, and drops everything and starts somewhere else.

Gene met us yesterday before Bible study, and they ran around,
came back here and planted garlic in the garden. He was at Susan's
watching TV when I got home from Renovaré. I wanted to get by
Trinity and check with Sherry on next steps, but did not have time.
But when Marie, Betty and I met for lunch, who should be sitting
in there, but Sherry! She is so sweet and so helpful. We set the
admittance date for July 22; I will go to Trinity next Tuesday to fill
out all the paperwork. I had told Brenda and Betty on Monday that
I was not having second thoughts about this, but I did
this morning.

2:00 PM: Well, no second thoughts now! He used the trimmer this
morning, but kept forgetting where he put it, and to clear off the
tangled grass; he needs help with everything he does. He took off
his clothes (at my direction) to take a shower, then just stood in the
middle of the bathroom for awhile as if he had forgotten what he
was doing—probably had—then he showered, and forgot to wash
his hair. That was about 20 minutes ago, and he is still wandering
around half-dressed. These actions make me more sure that he
needs to go to Trinity, so I have thanked God for them, even if I am
frustrated with them.

07.09.09   The young people from church were planning to
come here this morning to paint the fence, but It looks like rain
(again!) so we cancelled. This has been going on for weeks. I have
already sent the money to the church for their mission trip to

Romania, so even if the fence doesn't get painted, they have the money. John is a mess this morning. He is wicked with the trimmer: cuts what is not supposed to be cut, forgets where he has been, etc. Note: Doug just called and is going to try to line up the kids again for painting tomorrow morning. Hope it works this time! John seems to not understand anything I say; he just looks at me and there is no response. I have to go out and fill up the fuel tank, or give him water, but he is just blank-looking. I talked to Louise this morning, and she was telling me some of his actions at the store that don't make sense, but still insists that he is ok with her. I am not sure when or whether to tell her about Trinity. I know she will be upset, so I may try to keep it from her.

I was washing clothes this morning, and he took off his clothes in the kitchen. I have had to direct him to his closet 100 times! He has not made any sense today. He wanted to talk to me while I was studying for Bible study, so I said, OK. He told me he was not going to be working here anymore; he was going to get a job with (pointed to my lesson) and I said, Precept? He said, yes, he did not know what he was going to be doing, but he had to get another job. I assured him that he had retired, and did not need to get a job. Later he apologized and I asked for what? He said that while I was giving the shots.... could not finish his sentence. I told him he must have me mixed up with a nurse!

Here is Lucy's comment on my timing:

> I think you are wise to get him admitted to the facility asap. My friend told me that when her husband started fighting the mirror, the doctor and counselor told her to get him in the nursing home asap. You might want to get him in sooner because he could direct the anger at you. They are so confused that they don't know what they are doing and there is no sense in you trying to explain it because he doesn't understand it. They are not logical and you can't reason with them. Good luck.
>
> Love,
>
> Lucy R

I called Larry yesterday to let him know my decision, since he and I had talked back in May. He offered to do anything I needed, and I told him I would like to talk with him if I get a chance. This morning I called Pastor Stan to let him know, and he offered the same thing, and then prayed with me over the phone. Later I was talking to Doug about the fence painting, and let him know what is going on. He offered to do anything, and would go with me to take John if I wanted him to. How wonderful to have 3 pastors who care so much!

07.12.09   Doc appointment for chest x-ray on 10th; went well. Doc knew not to talk about Trinity. After doc, went to grocery store, then home. Worked garden for a while, had pizza as usual for Fri night, then to bed. Saturday spent cooking, readying for Ewans to come. Called Mother and sang Happy Birthday to her; made her happy. Sat on porch for a couple of hours, like old folks, waiting for Ewans to arrive! So good to see them all; had been too long! Susan and Roger came for dinner, and Sally and I talked on porch for a long time after the rest of family went down to Susan's and watched a movie. John and I went to bed about 10; rest of them slept at Susan's. So glad, because John had another episode of getting up, dressed, and walking noisily around the house at 12:30 AM. I got him back to bed, but it took me awhile to get back to sleep. Sally, Chip and Dempsey went to church with us, and Nigel and Parker went with Susan and Roger to their church. Spent afternoon in pool—nice day; John was quiet and just kinda watched everyone. I tried to pay attention to him, so he would not feel left out. When he did try to join in the conversation, it was hard to understand him. We all ate on our porch again this evening, then everyone went to Susan's to watch another movie, except Sally and me. We stayed here on the porch talking until almost 9. So nice to have her here; so blessed to have two wonderful daughters, and two wonderful sons-in-law! and three wonderful grandchildren! Thank you, God!

07.14.09   We had a nice visit and are so thankful for our family. It was good that the Ewans stayed at Jellum's since John was up twice in the night last night. I get *so* cranky when I cannot sleep, and when I hear him up, it rattles me so that I cannot get back to sleep after getting him back to bed. His voice is almost gone this morning; not sure what that means. He was talking about his "friends" (in the mirror) being angry and getting him. He asked me what the committee had decided... about the test... lots of things that just do not make sense. I am so weary; I think trying to understand him is as exhausting as taking care of him. He needs help continually now. I hate to feel this way, but I do keep thinking: only one more week! 8:45 PM: He has been really out of it today, worse than usual. After the Ewans left this morning about 8, he asked me what the committee had decided. I asked what committee? He said: about the testing... I have no idea what that was all about. Then when we got home this afternoon, he kept trying to ask me questions, and I would listen for 20 or so minutes, but he could never get out enough for me to know what the subject was, much less the question. Tom was with him from 10 until after 2 today, so I hope to find out what Tom saw. I went by and signed all the paperwork at Trinity, between Bible Study and Renovaré. I called Pastor Larry to see if he would meet Susan and me at Trinity next Wednesday to admit John, and he agreed. God gave me a phrase to use when we admit him: "your home away from home."

I pray it will be an easy transition. I almost wish it were tomorrow; today has been wearing.

07.16.09   The kids from church came yesterday to begin painting the fence, to earn money for their mission trip to Romania. There were five girls and one boy and his mom. Nice group. They did not finish, but just as well they quit, since we had a good rain shower about two hours later! It was a rough late afternoon; John kept wanting to say something to me, but couldn't articulate. frustrating for both of us! We went to church, always refreshing, then to bed. Joyce (sister) called; Don is taking a *long* time to heal. so sad... for her as well as for him. John and I went in to Roanoke today; took Louise to lunch and grocery. I left him with her, while I went to visit Cheri for a couple of hours. Got to see her precious son Tony—what a love! John was so confused coming home, not sure if he was with "the person I should be with" nor where he was going. Louise said he was talking to himself in her mirror, too.

I don't really want to wish him away, but some days are so tiring... Louise called later; she has fears of me admitting him to a home where he would be mistreated. I have not told her anything yet; may just wait until she finds out inadvertently. *She* tires me out!

07.17.09   Not an easy day; worked in the vegetable garden, and he wanted to help. I was pulling out the bean plants that had already been picked clean, and among them were lots of morning glories. They were all over the tomato plants, so I was having to be really careful not to disturb them. I was throwing the weeds and plants over the fence, and told John he could help by getting a wheelbarrow, and picking up the debris and hauling it into the woods. That was more than he could handle without continuous oversight by me. He ended up pulling up a couple of tomato plants, and knocking off five or six green tomatoes from other vines. I have noticed that many of his comments and questions that don't make sense have railroad terms in them, so he must be thinking of work. He came in the house before I did, and when I came in, he had moved chairs all around, including this office chair onto the back porch! and did not remember doing it.

07.19.09   How can I ever describe the range of emotions I have felt the past few days?! One minute I am looking at John, and thinking, What am I doing? and the next minute I am counting the days until Wednesday He has been like a robot: just moving through the day, watching me, trying to ask questions that make no sense. Saturday we worked in the yard again. He used the mower, but cannot handle the bag, so I had to keep helping him. At least he could feel useful! Saturday evening, Tom and Debi came over for dinner, and we had a relaxing time. At least three of us did; John was really restless. Most of what he said did not make sense, but they are nice, and responded anyway. A couple of times John made funny comments and we cracked up laughing. His wit is still intact at times. He kept talking about things that were not real, nor true, and seeing hallucinations. This morning in church, he fell asleep, again in Sunday school class, and again at the table after dinner. I kept thinking: this is our last Sunday afternoon together at home. But it was such a nice day, and I wanted to read outside, and he watched golf on TV. He came out every few minutes, and we had dinner at Susan and Roger's, so we were together a lot. I was able to talk to a few of our close friends at church this morning about Wednesday; asking for prayer. Joyce is coming to the facility and will sit in the parking lot and pray during our admitting him. I feel almost numb, and continue to pray that if this is not God's will, He will close the door.

07.20.09   2 PM: Well, this is our last day being at home all day. I invited Susan and Roger to come up for dinner tonight; I need Roger to help me do the TV exchange. I am eliminating two of the TV boxes and may change our choice of packages for channels. John has sat in a chair just staring into space, or staring at me most of today. I have been doing some house cleaning, and gardening for a little while. It is really cool today, especially for July in VA! I have been telling some of our friends (and my sisters) the timing of admitting him to Trinity Wednesday, so they will be praying for us. He seems so vacant today, I am not sure he would even understand what we are doing.

07.21.09   John's mom's 96th birthday today! I had the last lesson of I John this morning, and was able to ask several of the women for prayer for us tomorrow. John and Tom went visiting one of the sick church men, and then to lunch. Betty and I had lunch, and then John and I drove to Richfield to visit with Mother for awhile. She was so happy to see us; I plan to go more often. Even if she forgets by the next day that we were there, at least we

made her happy for the time we are with her. We spent the rest
of the afternoon with Louise, and then took her out to dinner for
her birthday; Susan and Roger met us at the restaurant. It was sad
sitting with him watching TV after we got home, knowing this was
the last time. I cannot imagine how I will feel tomorrow when I get
back home...

Admitting him to nursing home

07.22.09   Well, I am back home, and shaking like a leaf, as usual for these past few days. I did not sleep well last night. We had breakfast this morning, read the paper, read the Bible and prayed together as usual. Then I told him I wanted to shower, did he? and got him in the shower, then showered and as we were dressing, he was talking to "himself" in the mirror. Then he asked me what was on for today, and I said, "we need to talk about it." I went into the living room and sat down, and soon he came and sat with me. I will try to remember our conversation, although some of it is fuzzy right now.... "Honey, today we have reached another transition phase of our life together: Susan, Roger and I are going to take you to Trinity Mission this morning; it will become your home away from home." Silence, look of non-comprehension from him. "You want to be active, and you are so miserable here, just pacing around the house, moving things around, not knowing what to do with yourself. This will give you more people and activities, and friends can visit you there." Cry of anguish... more words of love and assurance from me... hugs and kisses... I also reminded him that he had scared me with some of his actions, and I needed some help taking care of him.

He asked what about church? "I will pick you up every Sunday morning to go to church; that will not stop."... He asked if his mom knew, and I said no. He wanted to call and tell her, but I said, let's wait until the next time we go to see her, and tell her face to face. He was ok with that. He said I guess I won't be going to the beach, then. "No, you were not going to be able to go anyway, with your night time walking around." Then he said, It seems the decision is made; let's go on and get it done. I told him it was too early, we were to pick up Susan and Roger at 10. He said, I respect you for making this decision. We left about 9:50, and Roger drove the car. John and I sat in the back seat holding hands, and he reminded me that I need to get the paperwork done when we have anything done to the car. (?) He cried out every now and then, and tears went down his face. I kept holding him, assuring him of my love, and trying not to cry myself. When we got to the parking lot, he saw Joyce and Pat in their car, and started crying again. They had come to pray, as had Gary and Margie, and I think Don and Joanne. Gene and

another man from our Sunday School class were there; Gene for
John, and Bobby to visit his brother-in-law. Larry was there when
we arrived, and was a God-send. John told him: When I heard this
decision this morning, I was against it, but seeing you here makes
me think God is in it. Larry prayed a sweet prayer for us before he
left. We were there about an hour—seemed like three hours—and
after I paid the bill, we went on the front porch. We hugged and
kissed goodbye, and I assured him I would be back this evening
to have dinner with him. As we left, we heard him say to a man on
the porch, My name is John Hartman, is this seat taken? Susan
and Roger asked if I wanted to go on home; and I said, not if there
is something you need to do in Rocky Mount. They wanted to go to
the library, so we did, then to lunch, then back home. I kept wanting to cry, but held it back. We went to buy peaches, and by the time
I got back to the house, I wanted to call Sally and my sisters, and
get some things ready to take back to him. So no tears yet. Susan
and Roger were wonderful; I am so thankful they had the time to
go and help.

I went back with more clothes and some cokes for John, and to
have dinner with him. That is when I thought *what have I done*?!
John looks so handsome and so young, with all those old people.
I almost cried right then in the dining room. We sat with a mom
and son; she was there for rehab, so was fine mentally. When John
tried to talk, I was assured once again that this was the right move.
I went to prayer meeting after leaving Trinity; when I saw Joyce

and Marie, I lost it again—they were so loving that I was able to get a grip. Then when people started praying for us, one after the other, I could not help but cry. I had not eaten much dinner, and with all the emotions I was experiencing, I thought I was going to throw up. I had to leave the meeting, and Joyce followed me, then Vickie and Melvin came out looking for us. They left and went to visit John. Others there told me they will go see him, too. Trinity is so close to so many of our church friends... thank God. I had six messages when I got home, and called Sally back. She was crying. Our phone message says: "Anne and John can't come to the phone...." and she got upset. I am ok right now (almost 10 PM) and will take a sleeping pill to be sure I get a good night's sleep.

07.23.09   I had a hard time falling asleep, but slept soundly for a change! It was weird to get up from our bed (I had been sleeping in a guest room) and have breakfast alone. I missed him a lot. The Renovaré group came out here this afternoon, and were such a comfort and delight. They all prayed for us, and several of them went by Trinity on their way home, to take some things to John. How blessed to have such friends!

07.24.09   What a morning! I was awakened at 6:30 am: "who in the world would be calling me at 6:30 am?! Oh no, it must be Trinity." It was. A nurse calling to tell me that John had tried to go out and had hit and kicked the workers trying to restrain him. They had to take him to the hospital to calm him down, and did not

know what would happen after that. I read that as: he might not
be welcome back here. So I got up, dressed, sent an email to Sally
and Susan (copied my Renovaré group on it for prayer) to let them
know, and got to the hospital a little after 7. He was in Emergency,
just lying on a bed quietly. They did several tests but the tests did
not show anything abnormal (or rather, *more* abnormal) so they let
me take him back to Trinity, where I stayed with him for several
hours. Nicki was there to do physical therapy, and she was so helpful; it was a blessing that she was there. I met his speech therapist
(not sure how much she can help him) Laura, who was very caring
and attentive to him. I need to pull together an album and pictures
to work on a "life line" book for John; Laura will work with him. I
sent an Awana plaque, a Master Gardener certificate, and a (Sail-
ing) plaque to hang on his wall, so visitors would know what his
interests are; he is having such a hard time verbalizing in a conversation. He has had plenty of company: Pastor Mark, Gale, Joyce,
Becky, Suzanne, Ronnie, Gene and Waylon (too much for one day?)
Waylon came by to take him out for lunch, but after the morning
excitement, I asked him to wait for a calmer day to take John out. I
told Way that I wanted to go to Columbus next Thursday for a few
days, and would appreciate his seeing John then; he agreed.

After I got home, I went down to Susan and Roger's to let them
know what was going on; Roger sent me the name of a place in
Martinsville that has lock-down unit for dementia patients. I
called Sally, who had called several times to see what was going on

with the hospital, etc. She cried while we were talking; we all trust God in this, it is just so hard! Then I called Cheri and Nancy; Joyce had called last night (all sisters) and was taking her husband Don to the doc today, so I will email her. Then Louise called, and I was able to tell her that John is in a nursing home. Because I was crying, I think it made her less volatile about it than she would have been otherwise. I talked to Larry and Ginger to let them know what was going on, and had several other calls of concern. Our church has proven themselves to be true children of God (1 John) by their love and concern for us in this ordeal.

07.26.09   I got a call from Trinity Friday night (after having gone to sleep!) that they have changed John's meds. A doctor saw him, and took him off Clonazepam, increased his Namenda, and added some med to help him sleep, and another to try to decrease his anxiety. When I went to see him Saturday after noon, he was like a zombie. He was in his room, staring into space, not making sense when he talked. I suggested we go out to the gazebo in the atrium area, and as we were going out, Gene and Bobby were coming to see him. Bobby went to get his wife Karen, who was visiting with her brother there, and then we all sat out in the gazebo. It was a beautiful day, and we enjoyed visiting with them, altho John did not talk much, and did not make sense when he did talk. I noted that he was talking "railroad" talk; he even told one of the residents that he lost his job, and a committee was meeting this weekend to decide if he had a new job. (Makes me wonder how

much stress he was under with NS). After about an hour, he asked
if we were going home, he needed to go. I realized he meant to
the bathroom, when he walked over into a corner of the yard, and
almost peed in the trash can. I got him back to his room in time,
and we then continued with our visit with our friends. After they
left, I got him back inside, and soon left to go into Roanoke to meet
Betty for our evening at an outdoor concert at the Fincastle Win-
ery. We picked up her friend Sally, and had a very pleasant evening
listening to Celtic music there. When we got back to Betty's, and
I went to my car to go home, I inadvertently locked my car keys in
the trunk of my car (!) and had to wait for AAA to come break into
my car! I was exhausted by the time I got home, only to find eight
messages on the phone. Two were from an angry Louise, wondering where I was. I had told her I would call her Sunday; I guess she
forgot. Turns out she called Susan's, and argued with Roger for ten
minutes about where had I gone, and why was I not at home. Roger
kept telling her I had spent the afternoon with John before going
to Betty's, but she seemed to not grasp that; only that I was out.

I did not sleep well, but got up this morning in time to get ready,
and go to Trinity to pick up John for church. He looked so nice
in his khakis and blue shirt and tie. Still fuzzy, but eager to go to
church. I called Louise on my cell phone, and handed it to John
to say hello to her, then did the same with Sally. I fed him what to
say to Louise, but he talked to Sally just fine. Everyone at church
who saw him was so glad to see him, lots of love poured out. He sat

with me, and slept during the message. At the end of the message, Joanne's husband Don took him down to the altar to pray with him. That touched us both; so kind. Went to Sunday School, and John himself asked for prayer. Tom M prayed a sweet prayer for both of us. Suzanne and her little granddaughter took us out to lunch, and we enjoyed that a lot. Then back to Trinity, to the gazebo, read the Sunday paper; John fell asleep and drooled all over his shirt. When we went back in, Nicki had come in with five-year-old darling Andrew, so we talked to them awhile before I left him in the community room to watch TV with other residents. I spend many hours on the phone when I am home, so many people caring about how we are doing. It is such a blessing. Pastor Stan sent an email after getting home from vacation, asking how things went. I sent him a couple of these entries; hope he won't be bored! He may not ask again! I got an email from Gary that I greatly appreciate:

> Oh Anne. the obvious question is, "why, God?" as happens so many times, no answer comes back to my question. then my mind reminds me, He knows what He is doing! He does all things well! all things for our good and His glory. that is a fact. i hang on it because it is fact. i need it to keep myself going. sicknesses, death, hurts - why? of course the answer is due to the fall, but why me? why my wife/daughter? and the answer is, 'why not?' how am i any different than anyone else? what do i have that i have not received? am i worthy of punishment/death/eternal destruction? in every way. only by His grace do i even breathe.

in my reading yesterday i was reminded that 'trials are always opportunities.' the fact is, i don't really want any more opportunities. spent 4 hrs in the e.r. last night with margie (pain in her side). found out the pain was nothing, but she has a cyst on her remaining ovary. more surgery? cancer? why margie again? why me? (no answer) He knows what He is doing!

when we arrived at trinity wed am, we parked and prayed and talked as we waited. neither of us had slept well that night, perhaps thinking of what would take place wed am. we agreed that this is so much harder than grace's death. she is gone. we can begin to heal.

its good to know that family and church are there and will be there. when you think it permissible, would like to take john for a ride, out to eat, by our home etc. whatever you think would be best.

do believe your getting away would be good. a break/ change of pace/scenery etc. do drive carefully.

know that we pray for your both and want to help. martha m is a grand lady to know.

our love,
gary

Martha M is a woman who went to their church; Grace and I had taken lunch to them one day about five years ago. Martha's husband Ron has now had Alzheimer's for 13 years! She called me

Fri night to tell me that he is at Trinity, and that she had met John there. We had a nice conversation—she *is* a grand lady to know! I look forward to seeing her there someday. I will not try to go tomorrow; Debi and others are going. I will go Tuesday and Wednesday and hope he is doing well enough that I can go to Columbus Thursday through Sunday.

07.27.09   Pastor Stan emailed me that he had gone to see John today, and John was OK. I stayed home, worked in the yard, and cleaned the porch furniture and the garage. Susan came up and had tea with me late in the afternoon; I enjoyed that! I got a call from Trinity, and when I returned the call, the nurse just said he was doing well, had been for a walk around the facility. I miss him, but I have to say that I don't miss all the confusion and difficulty of caring for him. Joyce S called to check on me today, and Marie, Barbara and Kris emailed. I am just awed at the love and care from our church family!

07.28.09   Another horrible day; had a meeting with a number of the staff at Trinity, led by a first class jerk. He immediately started in with all the bad things John has done and how I may need to find a place that is better for him, i.e., with special care for dementia patients. His manner was borderline rude, and I started crying so much the meeting was cancelled, and his boss, who is head of nursing there, came in. She was nice, and prayed with me, but I could not stop crying. I went back to John's room and stayed

with him for an hour, trying to let him know as best he can understand, how we may need to move him. I probably should not have
worried him with that, but I hope he can understand that he cannot go into other rooms. He had taken a urinal and poured it on the
man in the room next to him, and he had tried to get in bed with a
woman on the floor. Besides the terrible event of Friday morning. I
can see their point, but I am just sick about this. Anywhere else he
might go will be so far away. This is only 20 minutes away and so
convenient to us and to our friends. One of the therapists, Laura, is
being so helpful. She checked his file, and it says "Alzheimer's", not
Lewy Body, and the meds they switched him to after the Friday
episode are harmful to LBD patients. So I was able to meet the doctor, a nice young woman, and told her that he had been diagnosed
with LBD, and I was concerned about the meds he is now on. He
has regressed considerably. Joyce S. went back with me, and she
noticed a big difference since she saw him Thursday afternoon. I
am back home, after leaving him in the dining room with Martha
and Ron, and need to find his medical reports from the neurolo-
gists. I called Dr. A's office to ask them to please have the records
at Trinity corrected, and the woman I talked to there was not at all
helpful; she insisted that I have to deal only with Trinity people.
Even though he has been John's doc for seven years. I was *again*
pretty upset. I now wish I had just kept him at home, no matter
what the danger.

07.29.09   I got a call from one of the nurses last evening that they changed his meds again, but still had instructions that they could give him one of the anti-psychotic meds if he gets violent again. Then they called again at 6:30 AM to tell me that he had not slept well and they gave him Ambien in the middle of the night. I guess they need to keep trying to find meds that will work.

I spent a couple of hours this morning on the phone, with the insurance company and two nursing homes. I will visit both next week, depending on today's meeting results, and may take him out to Richfield so they can decide if they will take him; his record at Trinity may prevent another nursing home from taking him. I sent out an email to some church friends who have offered to "do anything" for us, and only heard back from 3 of them so far. I need a few to sit with him for an hour or so while I am in Columbus. I need to get away; it has been a couple of years since I got away without John.

8:30 PM: What a day! At least I was in better control today than yesterday, and I could feel the prayers of many friends lifting me up. I heard from more friends who will go see John while I am gone the next few days. I picked John up at 10:45 and we drove in to Roanoke. We picked up his records from the neurologist to take back to Trinity, then to grocery for Louise, then to her apt. We had a sandwich with her there, rather than going out. It was raining, and she and John both walk so slowly, I did not want to get them out. We visited for awhile; John was like a zombie. I am sure that the meds he is on are making him dopey. I met with the same group again this afternoon. The rude man made a gracious apology to me about his handling of yesterday's meeting. After he and his boss talked about 15 min., I said, "I am hearing the same thing I heard yesterday: you want me to find another place for John." They would not agree, but neither would they disagree. By the end of the meeting, they had called in the social services director, who brought me names of other nursing homes with more attention to dementia patients. I was ok, but disappointed that they did not seem to see that it was the change of environment and the mixed up meds that causes John's behavior there. The nurses and aides love him; they think he is so sweet. Which he is!

So I came home and called Richfield again, and talked to Pat who had helped us get Mother in there. I am going to go on the trip to Sally's; Trinity assured me they will take care of him, and not rush us out. They said they will help us get him in somewhere else. So when I get back Monday, I will go by there, and see how the weekend has gone. Tuesday, I will pick him up and we are going to Richfield to see that facility and have lunch there; they will do an evaluation of him while we are there, just watching and talking to him. I have asked for prayer for God's will to be done.

08.03.09   6:15 PM: Had a great visit with the Ewans! I was able to relax and get some good sleep, and enjoy them. We went to an outdoor theatre Saturday night: Shakespeare's *The Tempest*. That was fun. We also visited botanical gardens—wow! I bought Dempsey (and Sally!) a new sewing machine; D wants to sew. She is such a fast learner! I made her a dress; I wanted her to sew it up, but she wanted to wear it Sunday, so I made it quicker! Had not been to Columbus since Christmas; it was so good to see Jeanne, Kris, and Linda C.

Stopped at Trinity coming home; saw Sherry (admissions) and Vickie (director), who both immediately started talking about a new place for John. So even though he did ok over the weekend, they still think he will do better elsewhere. I called a private place in Roanoke ($$$!) and may go by there on the way home from Richfield tomorrow.

John seemed better than he was when I left, so maybe the wrong meds are getting out of his system. Way took him to driving range this morning; said John was great! Way and Gale seem to see a different John, or else they have seen many dementia people and know what to expect.

08.04.09　　　　I woke up praying, and was begging God to please give me wisdom, and guidance. I am not sure about sending out a fleece that if Richfield will accept him, that is where I will take him. The up side of that is that I will see my mother more often, also my sister in Salem. But I am also praying that if God wants me to just bring him home and get some help here, I will be willing and able to do that. I talked with Joyce S. this morning, and she prayed for us over the phone. I know God is there, and I trust Him completely, but I am not hearing Him. Pat called me back after a few minutes and encouraged me not to second-guess myself; that many prayers had already gone into this decision, the break had been made, and I should just rest in that. Interestingly, those were almost the same words that Susan used yesterday when I told her I was wondering about bringing him home.

My heavy heart was lightened by talking with Joyce and Pat, and I went on my way for what turned out to be a good day. I picked John up at Trinity, and we took Gale with us to pick up her car in Salem before we went to Richfield. We first visited with Mother for about 15 minutes... I had a call from her that she made 1 ½ hour after we were there, telling us to come see her! She is forgetting things so quickly now. But she was delighted to see us, so we made her happy for a few minutes. I prayed off and on all day as we spent time with the folks at Richfield, and then at the SML facility. We really liked both places, but there are three strong points in favor of Richfield: 1) Mother is there, so I will be able to see her more often. 2) We really liked the occupational therapist, who seems to connect with John and could help him with his speech and memory, 3) The administrator of the Richfield Memory unit (Joe) is a Christian and goes to the same church as Betty, and he had helped with the church building that Susan and Roger attend. Louise still needs help, and it is more convenient than having to go to the lake place, then to Roanoke. Also, I would see more of Cheri! The downside is the distance from home, and the fact that John will not have as many visitors from church as he would at SML place. He will have a private room in both places, as well as a nice, small dining room on his wing. I will "sleep on it" and make a decision tomorrow. If we choose Richfield, it will take place Monday Aug. 10th; if SML, maybe even sooner. I felt the prayers of all those friends and family today; we enjoyed our day. He was more coherent at Richfield than he has been in weeks, although by the time we returned to Trinity, he was wiped out, and stumbling as usual in his talking.

08.05.09   It was nice to have a leisurely breakfast, and go out on the porch to read the Bible and pray. They finally stopped the newspaper coming here, and now I don't go for the crossword puzzle right away in the mornings! I worked in the gardens awhile, watering them, and picked tons of tomatoes. I made some tomato sauce and put it in the freezer. I also worked on paperwork for admittance to Richfield for John, talked to our insurance agent, and talked on the phone to people calling about John. Our church is so wonderful and loving; so many calls, and emails, takes a lot of time, but I appreciate it so much. I called Norma, the woman who has been so helpful in taking Louise places when I cannot; we had a pleasant conversation. I went to see John about 4:30, and talked to his speech therapist, who thinks he did well in their time together today. He is still "on the railroad" in his conversation. I left about

6:15 to go to prayer meeting; what a blessing. I have felt comfortable today—no anxiety. I emailed Pat at Richfield to let her know that we do want to come there.

08.06.09   Another nice day... went to the peach orchards down the road, and bought a bushel of peaches for me, and one for Susan and Roger, then took the car in for service. Roger picked me up and brought me home. Got some tasks done at home, and then Susan picked me up and we went in to Rocky Mount. We went by to see John; I got the papers faxed to Richfield; went to lunch, then we got our hair cut. She invited me to have dinner with her and Roger; that was nice. I invited them to dinner for Friday evening. More phone calls to see how John (and I) is doing. Louise is a pest with her calling; she whines as if about to burst into tears, and it is hard to be patient with her. She asks questions, then interrupts when I try to answer. I will be checking out the possibility of getting her into the nursing home there one of these days soon. I pray that the doctor's office will get the papers filled out and faxed to Richfield tomorrow morning. I am meeting Betty in the morning, to hike and for lunch, and will go by the doc's office to pick up the originals and make sure they were faxed. I feel at peace; the prayers for us I am sure. I know people have been praying, so I am not sure why I have felt so anxious and upset before these past three days. I think the trip to Columbus helped me calm down, and the decision to go to Richfield has been made; also I wonder if my willingness to bring him home if that were the will of God, might have turned the corner for me. Now I feel, as well as *know*, God's presence and His peace. I keep thanking Him over and over.

08.07.09   A busy day, but productive! I went to see John today; sat with him in the gazebo. He kept trying to tell me something he had done that was bad, but could not express it to me in words I could understand. So I went to a nurse to see if she knew what he was telling me. She said that the person assigned to him last night did not know how to work with him, so they just assigned someone else; not to be concerned about it. Then I ran into one of the really nice young women, Hope, and she told me about it—it was her. He had tried to get into another room, and when she tried to guide him back to his room, he turned on her, grabbed her upper arm, and said, "I told you before!..." and it scared her. She said she did not report it, but did ask to be relieved. All he knew is that he did something wrong. He was pretty upset. I met Betty later, and we hiked for a couple of hours, and then went to lunch together. I stopped by to see that the doc's report was faxed to Richfield, and went on home. I had only been at home about 30 min., when I got a call that they needed me to come back and sit with him for a couple of hours.

So I did; he just keeps getting up and about for no apparent reason, and does not understand that someone must sit with him, to keep him from getting into trouble. We watched an old John Wayne movie, then I came home and fixed dinner; Susan and Roger came up and joined me for dinner.

08.09.09   I went to a brunch at Marie's with the other members of the Women's Ministry Team, planning for next year, and reported on Bible studies. It was a really nice time, with some of my best friends there. I worked in the garden and yard all afternoon; also talked to Dempsey on the phone to help with directions on a purse she is making. Did not hear anything from Trinity all day. I picked John up early this morning to go to church. So many people hugging him, glad to see him; he seemed rather vacant, but smiled. In the middle of the service, he whispered to me, "It is so nice to be here." We went to Sunday School, and out to lunch with Tom and Kris. By the time I got him back to Trinity, he was so tired. I hope he napped this afternoon. Tomorrow is moving day for us.

Moving to assisted living facility

08.10.09   The transfer to Richfield went well. I was at Trinity by 9:30, and one of the sweet young aides had packed up his things for him. I paid the bill, signed a form, and off we went. I had called Louise to let her know I would bring him by to visit on the way to Richfield., so we spent about an hour with her. I made sandwiches and we had lunch there. We arrived at Richfield about 12:40, so John and I went to see Mother first. She was glad to see us; had obviously forgotten that we had been there last week. It takes about ten minutes for John to walk from his building to hers. Of course, he can't go unless someone is with him. Kris met us there and helped us get his room set up; it is private, with a private bath, and very nice and clean. I need to get a single bedspread for his bed. I stayed until about 5:45, and then went to Cheri's for the night. Had a nice visit with her, but stayed up too late talking!

Got back to Richfield Tuesday morning about 9:30; John had been dancing in a group activity. The activity director, Brenda, said he will make her job easier; he will be a big help. He seems to be ok; has trouble finding his room, but there are always people to help him. Lots of older women there; most are mobile. There are seven men, most use walkers, but some are mobile. Everyone of course has dementia of some sort. We met several of the therapists; he will not need physical therapy, but will get occupational therapy and speech / memory therapy. I had lunch with him Tuesday, and we walked over to see Mother. We sat outside in the garden area for awhile, too. I left about 5pm to go to Betty's for the night. She was in a class, so I read a book until she got home. Went back to Richfield by 9:30 today; he was dancing again! He is so young and so good-looking, I can see that many are not sure he is a resident. Joe M, the admin., is such a nice man; so kind and helpful to everyone. A local church group came over at 2 and held a nice service for about 15 of the residents. Brenda asked if they could come one morning a week and have a men's Bible study, and they agreed. She asked John to help her with it; he readily agreed. I left about 4pm; was so tired, and just wanted to get home. I have been thanking God for this move; even with all the hurt and anxiety about Trinity, I believe God was in it, to get John somewhere that he could get help and be more content. I plan to spend a couple of days, or partial days there each week.

08.13.09   It was good to be home again last night, and sleeping in my own bed. Although the guest bedrooms at Cheri's and Betty's were like home! I was able to work in the garden for a little while this morning, before going out to meet Kris for lunch. I went by Trinity to take back (and hopefully get reimbursed) some of John's unopened, and unneeded meds. I ran into a number of staff and one resident who asked about John, said they missed him, and to tell him hello. Tom Q was very helpful, and asked if John was better off now. I agreed that he was, and Tom gave me a hug. Kris and I had a nice lunch and talked about how we would "team teach" this fall. I am happy to let her teach, and I will back her up, as well as take care of the roster, paying for the study guides, etc. Roger was mowing the lawn when I returned, and Susan and I had iced tea on the porch. A nice day, feeling more relaxed than in months. Praise God for his perseverance and love.

08.14.09   Emailed Audra at Richfield to see how John is doing; here is her response:

> Hi Anne,
>
>   John is adjusting *very* well. He paced a little after you left Wednesday, but then began interacting with other residents and staff. He did very well yesterday. Brenda had him outside

yesterday morning helping her stake tomato plants and assisted with other gardening activities. He went on the mystery ride yesterday afternoon and did very well. He is very pleasant always wanting to help the staff or other residents. Appetite is very good. We have not experienced him with any exit seeking. We are working on other activities that he may enjoy doing.

Have a good day. Feel free to contact us anytime.

I rearranged the furniture in our bedroom back to the way it was before I made it easier for John to get around. I like it better as it is now. I worked in the yard for hours this morning, but wiped out by 3:00! So I took it easy this afternoon, reading on the porch. A good day; my mind is not running in circles, now that I know John is being cared for.

08.17.09　　　I had a wave of nostalgia sweep over me as I drove to church on Sunday morning, realizing anew that John would not be going with me any more. I arrived at Richfield about noon, and he was getting back from chapel; he had helped get some of the wheel-chair-bound residents there and back. We had lunch, actually, I rarely eat with them (too many carbs!) but sit and drink cup of coffee. I did have a sandwich with him today for lunch. We walked over to see Mother and she walked part of the way back with us. I went to see her today, but after I left John; the sky looked like a big storm so I drove. After seven hours yesterday and six today, I was emotionally/mentally exhausted. I did take crossword puzzles and a book to read, but feel like I should be giving John attention instead. We listened to some classical music on the radio for awhile, and then went for a walk and sat by the pond some. I called Sally's number, and he talked to Parker and Dempsey. After he hung up, he was almost crying. He asked/stated, "I am not going to get better, am I?" I told him only with a miracle. He said, "I guess I will just live here until I die?" I just tried to comfort him, but it is so hard to know what to say.

I met Barbara R for dinner at Ippy's and we had a nice dinner and conversation. Her mom is at Trinity, and she is having a rough time, too. Louise evidently forgot that we had agreed that I would call her, and she was not to keep calling me. She called over at Betty's and today called here, and then called Susan and Roger's, too. I called her this evening, and reminded her not to call around trying to find me. She agreed again, but it won't last long, I am sure.

08.18.09 8 AM: I woke up feeling bad about being impatient with Louise. As a friend once said, "She can step on your last nerve!" and how true that is! But I don't want to be rude to her. As I sat down for breakfast alone, I realized I miss John so much, but I miss the John that used to be. He is lost to me now. I was talking yesterday to Barbara about how mine and John's relationship was so much of "doing" things: sports, making things, yard and garden, etc. I will just try to be grateful for those years we enjoyed doing things together, and not lament the loss of those days. Susan called to see how he is doing. She is a comfort to me in my aloneness. Not loneliness, thank God, just aloneness. There is a difference! I think Betty feels loneliness, and I pray for God to comfort her.

Just received a response from Audra at Richfield:

> Hi Anne,
>
> John is adjusting very well. He seems to be doing well at night. Staff has stated he is not exit seeking but he does walk the hallways. He is pleasant with staff and others residents. No problems noted.
>
> Thanks,
>
> Audra

And a new message Aug. 20:

> Hi Anne,
>
> John is doing just fine. He went to Famous Anthony's for breakfast with the residents. Brenda said he did really good. He has been interacting with other residents well. He has been assisting Joe with some small tasks (such as fixing the gliders on the bottom of walkers). Yesterday, he was trying to tell us how long you all had been married. He often speaks of his love for Christ and of his family. He seems happy. I know it has to be hard

to be so far away. I will not be here next week, but feel free to call anytime to check on John.

Thanks,

Audra

08.22.09   This has been an interesting week since leaving John at Richfield on Monday afternoon. I can't get used to being all alone, but I do not really feel *lonesome*. I am not eating well, so I need to work on better nutrition. And if I am not working in the garden/yard, I am not getting exercise. I feel almost disoriented with my life—like I am just in a waiting pattern. I went to church Wednesday night, to a dinner Friday night, and to the Swartzes' this morning, but have been home the rest of the time. The three couples at the dinner (Sunday School class members) made me feel welcome, not like odd man out, and it was a very enjoyable evening. Being with Gary and Margie was nice this morning, too. I had let Gary's birthday slip by, and so invited them for dinner in Sept. to celebrate. I am reading a lot; still have not watched TV since John left July 22! Finished *London* by Edward Rutherfurd, and now reading *The Worst Hard Time* by Timothy Egan, about the Dust Bowl of the 1930s. Sad...

08.24.09   Finished the dust bowl book; maybe should stop reading for awhile and get some things done!

Went to church yesterday; service and Sunday School were focused on our upcoming church year, using E412 as the catch phrase, meaning Exodus, Eccles., and Ephes. 4:12. At the end of the worship service, pastor called for those who wanted to dedicate themselves to whatever God has planned for them, to come to the altar and pray. I did, and was between Becky and Vickie. Becky put her arm around me, and was so loving, that I felt the tears come up. I prayed that God will show me what He wants me to do, and got back to my seat. I did cry some, missing John at church, feeling the love of the members for us, etc.

I picked up Louise and we went to lunch before going to Richfield. Tom and Kris were there with John when we got there. Cheri brought Mother over after awhile. John had had a negative experience that morning, but none of us could understand whatever he was trying to tell us. He struggled with words for a couple of hours off and on, but never could articulate the problem. It seemed to have to do with his going to Chapel that morning. Louise enjoyed being with us all, and John introduced her to several of the staff and residents. At one time, he joked, "I am trying to figure out how to get her in here, and me out of here." We all laughed. I stayed with Betty overnight, and got back to Richfield by 8:15 Monday morning. We saw Joe, and I think he solved the mystery: he had taken John out off the grounds on a walk last week, so John thought he should be able to go out. It seems that John had to wait at the chapel after service for someone to take him back to his building, and he did

not like having to wait. Waylon came to see John about 10:30, so I
went over to see Mother for awhile. Waylon told us that Gale had
broken her foot while on a "good will" trip with someone; she had
prayed for God to direct her in what to do to lessen her load. He
answered by making her stay in place for awhile! Like my praying
for God to help me curb my tongue, and He allowed me to get a bad
case of laryngitis the next day! After I left Mother, I met my broker
and her assistant for lunch; nice women, and enjoyable time with
them. Lots to do this week to get ready for the beach trip, and go
back to Richfield Friday.

08.28.09   Well, I went back to Richfield on Thursday instead:
I had a call from the nurse at R, letting me know that John's glucose level was 44. That did not mean anything to me, so I asked, "Is
that good or bad?" It was bad, normal being between 70 and 120. I
was with him when they did the blood test, and did not notice that
he was particularly tired, but they are now taking a reading twice
a day. It was 70 the next test. Anyway, they suggested I take him
to the doc, so I made an appt. for Thursday afternoon to see a new
doc, who is at the clinic on the R campus. I had worked in the yard
and garden Tuesday and Wednesday, and met a friend for dinner
Wed evening before church. She and I went on to church for prayer
meetings and a business meeting. I met Kris Thursday morning for
brunch before going by Louise's and on to Richfield. John seemed
ok while I was there, but was, as usual, hard to converse with. He
seems to have lost two thirds of his vocabulary; even though he

looks as if the thoughts and words are in his head, they just don't come out. I mentioned that our Music Minister Ken told me how much he likes John, and is so sorry about this situation, and John got tears in his eyes. When I mentioned that one of the teenagers plans to come see him, he actually had tears running down his face. I almost cried myself. The doc was fine; will try to figure out why the glucose reading was so low. We went by to see Mother for a short visit. I left about 4:00 to go to the Davies for dinner. They invited me to join them with the Scotts, since Gale broke her foot, and should not be standing and cooking. I had taken chicken salad and tomatoes over to them on Wednesday. It was a nice dinner and pleasant evening. But boy was I tired by the time I got home! Being with John, and with Mother, is so emotionally and mentally exhausting. Today, I put up tomato sauce and green beans, and did more prep for the beach trip. I missed John so much this afternoon...

09.06.09   Arrived home from the Outer Banks about 1 PM today; rode back with Susan and Roger. Left last Sunday; rode with Ewans. They came in on Saturday, went by Richfield to see John. They were surprised at how he looked, i.e., tired and old, and how unfocused he is. I had a call from Tom C. while at the beach, asking if he could take John out to lunch Friday. I called Tom Saturday morning to see how it went. Tom said he took John in to Salem, but John was ready to go back to R as soon as he ate. I wonder if he feels more secure there, than being out. Mother always is ready to go back when we take her out. We had an enjoyable week. I am glad Susan and Roger went this year, not only because we enjoyed their being with us, but it made it not quite as noticeable that John was missing. They took the bedroom John and I usually have, and I slept downstairs with the Ewan family in the 4th bedroom, adjacent to Dempsey's! She is so precious. It is such a delight to be with all of them, and I thank God that we all get along so well. Especially since it rained 4 days we were there! Crossword puzzles, jigsaw puzzles, Scrabble, Chronology, and books! Very little TV—hooray! We did have nice days the last two, although the surf was pretty rough. A number of things made me miss John so much, but I do realize I am missing "the John that was." I am starting to be more aware of how much we are missing in retirement, not being able to enjoy each other. We had such a good time with our tennis, golf, boating, gardening... At least we can remember those good times; or I hope he can. The house is so quiet now; I don't really enjoy TV, and it is hard to get radio inside the house. I need a good CD player! I feel rather melancholy, but not unhappy. I am so thankful for family and friends, and especially for Jesus Christ.

09.07.09   Labor Day; seems like Memorial Day was just a few weeks ago. I labored all day! Cleaned house, did lots of laundry, worked out in the garden,, picked beans and tomatoes and peppers, and shared with Susan and Roger. Worked on the lawn mower, but cannot find, in all the hundreds of screws and nuts, the right size to replace the screws that fell out. Talked to Betty, Nancy, Brenda and Joyce S. today; thanking God for friends!

09.10.09   Found out that Sally has a blood clot in her leg, perhaps from the long ride in the car to the beach. Scary to think about it; she went to hospital, and is now taking coumidin, off oral contraceptives, and giving herself shots. I find myself praying often for her. I have spent a lot of time this week about Mother's situation; costs for Richfield have gone up, so we had to do something to reduce the costs. After many conversations with sisters, I met with Pat at Richfield to see what could be done. Since Mother has been there two years in October, we can apply for a subsidy for her, which will mean she has to share a room with another resident. Cheri and I plan to move her next week; it will be difficult to try to explain all this to her.

I spent Wednesday with John; took him to a new neurologist, to see his mom, and back to Richfield. I like the doc—Dr. Bell—a black woman who seems to be a very good doc. She gave John a number of verbal tests, and a couple of written tests. He did not do well on the verbals—did not know what day it was, nor how old he is, nor what year it is. She asked him to write a sentence on a piece of paper; he wrote, and then read it aloud: "Jesus Christ is my Lord and Savior." I almost cried; she responded that He was hers, too! I told the prayer group at church that night, and Stan wants to use that story in his message Sunday! I also told the prayer group how blessed we are that he is still getting so many visitors from the church, even if it is so far to drive. A Salem church group goes to his building every Wednesday afternoon and holds a short service for the residents. They plan to work with John on Wednesday mornings to have a Bible time for the men there; John was pleased that they asked him to help with it. Not sure what he can do, but at least he can pray! He and I read Psalms and prayed together while I was with him. Friends have asked me how I am doing, and I have to stop and think. I am doing ok; not eating well, but plan to try to correct that! I miss him; the house seems empty. But being with him for even a short time at Richfield reminds me of why he needs to be there, and not at home. He has been leaving his room during the night, and using the hallway as a "bathroom." We moved his bed so that when he gets up, he sees the bathroom, and I asked that the night staff be sure to leave the light on in the bathroom for him at night.

09.12.09   Had Susan and Roger up for waffles for breakfast. Roger took the guard off the lawn mower for me; it kept getting loose and the blade was hitting it, bending the blade and the guard. So I mowed grass, raked, mulched for several hours today. It was a beautiful day. The "mail lady" stopped and asked how we are doing; she said she prays for us both. I thanked her; it is so nice to know that there are so many lifting us up in prayer! Sally is doing well now; I hope she will not get another clot! Today was a beauti-

ful almost Fall day; I sat on the porch and read a book
this afternoon.

09.13.09   Pastor Stan used John in his message today, and I
got a lot of nice comments about John's witnessing. I hope he will
understand how much that meant to people when I tell him tomorrow. Tom and Debi went to see him yesterday; one of the women
residents kept following Tom around. John told Tom to ignore her;
she was union! LOL! He is on the railroad often these days.

Trouble with mother

09.15.09   Had a nice visit with John yesterday; we spent
time with my little friend Bee (dementia patient) and her husband
Norris in the living area. Gene came to see John, then Pastor Stan,
then Alton came. Alton was one of John's first Awana boys, and
he is now 18! What a great kid! I've picked him out for Dempsey!
I had picked Mother up at her facility, and brought her over to
visit with John and me, while Cheri got into her room and started
cleaning out what she could. Mother has enough in that little
room to fill the back of a pick up truck, and I am not talking about
furniture! I left about 4:45 and went to Betty's; she and I went
to an After 5 Business Women's Dinner together, and that was
enjoyable. I stayed overnight at her house, and got up early to get

to John just after breakfast. He and I went over to start moving more of Mother's things, and she did not remember that Cheri had told her she would be moving. She did not even remember Cheri's being with her for several hours Monday. We finally got her into the Bible study, and Rafael and Cheri came to help with the move. We all four worked for almost three hours, and threw out a lot of junk. Mother was so upset; she asked over and over what was going on, and why could she not live with one of her daughters. I kept patiently answered her for the first hour or so, then got irritated with her. So I tried to pray for her, with my arms around her, telling her I loved her. She seemed to think I was doing this to her.

No matter how many times I answered her two questions, she would forget the answers within a few minutes. I was emotionally exhausted by the time we got her in there. I can't say "settled in there" because she was still miserable hours later. She called Cheri, then me, to tell us that "they" had moved her into another room with someone else, and she did not like it. So it was a rough day. I was able to get to Renovaré late, and Suz and Joyce were wonderful, letting me vent, and encouraging me. I was so tired when I got home, and realized I had only eaten a breakfast bar and an apple pie all day long. So I fixed a nice easy meal at 4:30, and felt better. I talked to all 3 sisters to keep everyone in the loop. Cheri agreed to be the POA for Mother, since she is here and I have POA for Louise and John! I called Louise and tried to let her know what was going on with both John and Mother, but she kept interrupting me, and

I got frustrated with her, too. I told her she was butting in every time I tried to answer her questions, and asked if she could not hear me talking. She apologized, then I apologized for being snippy. So we are still friends. It seems that one of the women there has been after John, and I am not sure what happened. He seemed to think he had done something wrong, but could not get it out. She was crying as I left Monday, so I hugged her and tried to make her feel better. She said she did not have any friends. Maybe I should spend even more time there, to be friendly to some of those folks.

09.18.09 A whole day at home! Wonderful, restful! First day in several weeks for me. Yesterday was our second lesson in the Precepts Revelation Part 4 study. Kris and I again did team-teaching; both of us were worn out, her from Tom being in the hospital all week, and me from my mother's move to a new room at Richfield. We seem to do well teaching together; probably because both of us are so grateful to have the other as a teacher! I had Gary, Margie, Betty, Susan and Roger here for an early dinner, to celebrate a late birthday for Gary. The meal was one of the best I have done in awhile; most of it from my garden. The fellowship and conversation was great, too. Today I did laundry, ironing, all the housework duties that have not been done in awhile. I have talked to my sisters often lately, especially because mother is not taking the move from private to semiprivate room well at all. She calls us several times a day, telling us the same thing over and over. She forgets that we are the ones who moved her, so she begins by telling us "they" moved me, and continues on and on about how she doesn't understand, she doesn't like it, she wants to live with one of us, etc., etc. It gets so wearing. Being emotionally tired is worse than being physically tired. I am getting bills almost daily from John's situation, and so far, no reimbursement from insurance for his being in a facility. I will have to follow up on that soon. I am still waiting to get my Social Security payments straightened out; so far I have lost over $2,500. I am not worried about it, but I do wish it could get worked out; I have enough to do! Just received this message from my sister:

> I went to see Mother around 3pm today. I took some of her clothes I had washed and helped her organize her closet and drawers. There was a concert by a young man playing the piano and a young lady playing the violin. It was not hymns but Mother seemed to enjoy it anyway though she much prefers hymns. I stayed for the concert (about 30 min.) and then we sat in the sitting area in her new hall for a short time; met another resident of Ivy—Frankie (a woman). She seemed nice. Mother kept telling me how nice I was to people so I hope she got the message. She was *much* more pleasant. I hope things go well and she can adjust to this new place.
>
> Love,
>   Cheri

09.21.09   Update on mine and John's visits with Mother:

Sunday visit: we got to her place as she was finishing her lunch, so

we sat on the sofas and visited for awhile. She kept asking me if I

wanted to see her room, and I kept telling her I had seen it. That I

had helped her move into it. Every time we went through that, she

said, "I didn't know that!" She was relatively (compared to last

Tuesday) pleasant. Even asked John how he liked his place. He

shrugged and said it was ok, and she said, "I guess you like it about

like I like it here," with a smile. Once in a while she makes sense!

We stayed about 30–40 minutes, and he got restless, so we went

back to his building.

Today we went over to see Mother about 1:45, and I took several

pastries that we had left from the MC&E (John's unit: Memory

Care and Enrichment) "celebration" of Assisted Living Week. I got

her to come into the little cafe in her building (She "Did not know

it was there!" and we got some coffee and had a "tea party." John

introduced himself to the two women at the other table, and actu-

ally sat down with them. (Smart guy!) Turns out it was Nikki and

Sue, her companion! Mother did not even recognize Nikki, after

sharing a room with her for a week! Sue took John in to the room

with the TV and turned it on for him. Mother and I went in with

him after we (I) chatted with Sue and Nikki awhile. Mother said,

Don't you want to go into my room and visit? and I said, No, I like

to be out here with others. Then she started in again over and over about how she did not like having someone in her room, and had already forgotten who Nikki was, and that she did not understand why she could not live with one of her daughters. I got up and told John, "Let's go back to your place; I do not need to listen to all this again." and Mother and I walked out into the hall. She was confused about why I was upset with her, and I tried (*again*) to tell her we were all tired of her going on and on about this situation.

She said, "Tell me again why I can't live with one of you." and I said, OK, one more time: and went through Joyce, me and Cheri again, not mentioning Nancy. As soon as I stopped talking, I said, now, can you tell me what I just told you? She looked sheepish, and said No. I said, See, Mother that is why you need to stop asking these questions, and just accept it. You can't remember the answers. She said (again) Well, I just won't tell you how I feel if you don't care. I told her I *knew* how she felt, I do care, but she has told us 100 times! Of course she argued with that, too. John had disappeared at that point, so we had to go find him. She walked to the desk with us, and wanted to walk to our car with us. I had to tell her twice that we had walked over from his place. Oh, where is he? she asked for the 10000th time. I feel like printing out all the answers to all her repetitive questions, and having them handy, and saying, read #2 or #5 or whatever. And if she asks me again about living with us, I am going to remind her that she does not like living with Nikki!

As we were leaving, Betty told me that she is doing the dishes clean-up again. They don't like it, but are dealing with it. I told Betty the first glass or dish that breaks, they can "fire" her. As I walked back with John, I told him "Thank you for being so sweet about living here." I stayed until 4:00 with him; he is trying to make friends with the other men there. They had a Bible study Wednesday morning, and he participated. He tried to help those who need help with wheelchairs and walkers. None of the men can really carry on a conversation, but he tries. I met many of the family members today at the "celebration" and they all had nice comments to make about John. He was sitting on a bench, talking to one of the men as I left. What a sweetie. I was supposed to take Louise to the grocery after I left Richfield, but I called Louise, and she said she was ok until Saturday. I was so glad; I am wiped out! I found out how he can get ESPN and Monday night football, at his request, and hope he can get it tonight. He really doesn't understand how the TV works anymore.

I will go back Saturday, picking up Louise to go, too. They are having a "Goodbye Summer" party/ cook-out. I may go Friday and stay overnight again. I will go to our church JOY club (retirees) meeting tomorrow; the speaker is the head of the Roanoke Alzheimer's Association, and I want to hear what she has to say.

09.22.09   She was a board member, and was really just acquainting us with the role of the Association. The speaker who actually spoke on the disease and the role of caretaker was a man whose mother is now at Trinity. He took care of her at home for years, and his talk was really good. I could relate so closely to his comments, especially the time of admitting her into the nursing home. I cried then, and was glad I was sitting next to Gale, who is so loving and such a comfort. I came home and called Roger to see if he would come get my trimmer started for me. He did, and even though it was drizzling rain, I spent about an hour and a half, cutting the tall grass under the fence that I cannot get to with a mower. After I finished, I could hardly hold a pencil, for the shaking of my hands and forearms! That was my first time with that piece of equipment! I worked on medical bills and insurance forms in the later afternoon, and talked on the phone. All of this with Mother has drawn us sisters closer, and it is nice to talk to them so often. I feel bad about my being short with Mother on Monday, but she called yesterday, and did not mention the room or coming to live with us. So maybe, she got the message. I had thought of bringing her to the cookout at John's place Saturday, but I would have to devote all my attention to her, instead of John and Louise, and meeting the other families. One thing about Louise: she will make herself at home!

09.25.09   Worked in John's workshop Wednesday; hope I can find a good home for all these woodworking magazines. I cleaned the floor and stacked some of the wood; hope I can find a good home for the wood, too! Had to teach the Precept lesson by myself

Thursday: Kris could not leave Tom alone. I pray the docs can find whatever is causing his blackouts. Gale took me to lunch for my birthday after Bible study. I am amazed at how she and Waylon have taken us under their wing! Way was planning to take John out to a driving range today to hit a bucket of balls, but it is raining. I have been working on the transfer of clothes, summer to winter. I will take John some fall/winter things tomorrow when I go. I did go see him yesterday after Gale and I had lunch; arrived there around 2:15, but he had gone out with some of them to lunch and did not get back until after 3:00. He looked worn out when he got back, and was grippy and difficult the whole time I was there. I did his laundry, and tried to help him learn how to use the TV. That was trying; he seemed to not even know what TV was, much less how to turn it on, and change channels. It was very frustrating; I told him to call one of the staff whenever he wants to watch it in his room. I think he spends most of his time out of his room, which is good. I felt so terrible driving back home, I almost wished I had not gone. I asked him for a smile as I was leaving, and he smiled for a moment. Not sure how aware he was of anything.

09.29.09   Took Louise with me to the Richfield Memory Care "Summer into Fall" party. The weather was rainy, so we had to be indoors. It was nice; lots of family there with residents, although there are some who never seem to have any visitors. Louise enjoyed it, and was cute. Even John was proud of her. He was in better spirits than he was on Thursday. I think Louise could really

see why he is at Richfield; he is so out of it. We stayed until about
4 PM, then I took her on to the grocery. I was so tired when I got
home about 6pm. Refreshed at church Sunday morning, praise
God. Had a call from a staff member when I got home from church:
another resident walked into John's room at 11 PM Saturday night,
and they got into it. I am sure that scared John, remembering how
paranoid he was about someone breaking into our house when he
was here. Had another call last night that another resident pushed
John into the wall. He was not hurt; evidently, they were shaking
hands, and the guy would not let go of John's hand and hurt it.

It has been nice to be home the last couple of days, cleaning house,
working in the garden and yard. I was raking black walnuts up
across the street; there must be thousands! I had to quit when my
hand, elbow and shoulder started really hurting. Margic and Gary
had a birthday dinner for me last night, with Betty, Susan and
Roger there, too. It was very nice; she is so sweet. Waylon and Rodney (son) are coming over this evening to try to get my TV working
again. I don't have much hope for it, but I am glad they are willing
to try. Rodney is a woodworker, so I plan to offer him some of the
books, and some walnut if he wants them. Mother is still calling
about not being happy in her semi-private room, and I keep trying
to be patient with her. Actually, she has not called since Sunday.

10.01.09   Way and his son were able to get the TV working again; so I watched the news for the first time in over two

months. I usually just keep the classical music channel on. Right
after I wrote that Mother had not called, she did! But for the first
time since moving her into the semi-private room, she did not
complain—hooray! She was very sweet, and I told her I would see
her Sunday. I had planned to go after Bible study, but Susan and
Roger are doing the semi-annual hay cutting, baling and storing,
so I helped them. We worked Wednesday afternoon, and I came
home from Bible study (and a haircut) to help again, rather than
going to Richfield. We had two absolutely beautiful days in which
to work in the fields. I got a call from Audra, director of resident
care, late this afternoon: she and/or Joe will be taking John to a
psychiatrist tomorrow. He has declined so quickly lately that they
hope the doc can prescribe something to help him. I had noticed
that he seems more distant, and also more agitated, every time I
see him. Audra thinks the psychiatrist will know better what to
prescribe for John than the other docs who have seen him. I told
her I would come in, and go with them, but she said not to. I could
not tell if she did not *want* me to come, or was being cognizant of
my having to drive in so far. I said several times that I could come,
but she said they would need to be there to tell the psychiatrist
how he has been acting, and how he has declined. Louise has called
a couple of times today, and I got frustrated with the last call, as if
she knew more than the medical personnel how to treat him. I told
her we have to trust them, and hung up. She did not call back. I felt
bad, but not bad enough to call her back. It is so hard to talk to her;
she never listens. I talked to Betty and to Gale, and they both made

me feel better. Note from Marie, after Donnie visited John again today: "Donnie noticed in the past two weeks that John has been 'different'. Today Donnie said John cried a lot. Last week he was distracted. So he has seen a difference."

Declining rapidly

10.02.09   I got up this morning, praying that I would know whether I should go meet them at the psychiatrist office today. I asked God to please say yes or no in a way that I would understand. After a while, He let me know that He was causing the anxiety in my soul as a way of letting me know that I needed to go! So I went. and glad I did. I could then see why Audra was reluctant to have me there; on the way into the exam room, she said to me, "I hope I don't upset you with what I need to tell the doc, but I need to be honest in telling about his behaviors lately." I assured her I would not be upset with whatever she needs to say. The doc is a young black woman, who specializes in psychiatric and geriatric medicine. She tested him the same way he has been tested a number of times; he did not know what year it is, what month it is, how old he is, etc., etc., but was able to answer correctly the name of Roanoke when asked in what city we were. He tried to talk several times, but never did make sense. I learned from Audra that he is becoming incontinent, and is behaving inappropriately to some of the women, as they are to him, too. He is agitated frequently, is beginning to have tremors, and cries lately. After about an hour of testing and discussion, Dr. B. decided to take him off Aricept, and put him on Exelon, which works better for Lewy Body Dementia. She also decreased his dosage for Depakote, to increase slowly, for the behavior and depression. I talked to her about the difference in taking him to a psychiatrist vs. a neurologist, and she explained the difference. I commented that it seems to me he would be better off with her than the neurologist and she only said, that is up to me. But when she was talking about different meds, and reactions, I could tell she knew her stuff, so I opt for her. I will cancel the neurologist appointment scheduled for Dec. and I made another one for Dr. B. I took Audra and John back to Richfield, and stayed with him the rest of the day.

He and I went to see Mother; she thought I was Nancy, but was delighted that we came, whoever I am! John got restless after 15 or so minutes, so we walked back to his building. I did his laundry; he tried to help, but put his dirty clothes in the trash can in the laundry room. I don't handle those behaviors well; I need to be more patient. There was a party in the afternoon for a woman who just turned 100! Waylon came, and we had ice cream together. I introduced Way to some of the staff. He is such a good friend. We were able to spend some time chatting with Paul (not a talker) and Joe before I left. I thank God for that staff! and for our church friends! It has been noticed by many of the staff how often our church friends visit!

10.05.09   I finally had a real melt-down, although Sally told me to call it a "break down" instead. I think I cried/prayed for an hour when I left him Sunday afternoon. As I was driving to church Sunday morning, I once again realized how much I miss him going to church; I even "saw" him in my mind's eye, standing at the door in his suit, smiling and handing out bulletins. I got choked up then, but went on to the service ok. I kept feeling my throat close up, as it I were going to cry. I left before Sunday School, to get to Richfield to go to chapel with him, and arrived there about 10:30. He was lying on his bed, and Sandra, CNA, was in the room with him. He had walked down the hall, started to undress, and had defecated on himself. Sandra took him back to him room, got him in the shower, cleaned his clothes, etc. He said his stomach was upset; I guess it was the meds. Although several others were sick, and as it turned out, there was a lock-down in another bldg. because of the flu. They did not take any residents to chapel, and asked if I would have a short service for them. So I read Psalm 23, and prayed for them. A volunteer asked me to lead them in the Lord's Prayer, and I began, but started crying in the middle of it. When we went in to eat lunch,

I realized John had forgotten how to use the utensils, and how
to pick up and set down his drinking glass. He would set it in his
food. He had a hard time getting food on his fork or spoon, and got
irritated with me trying to help him. I think he was embarrassed.
I noticed when we were outside, he kept trying to pick up shadows,
as if they were things. He stepped high over designs in the carpet.
He urinated on himself three times while I was there; I did two
laundries for him. I had planned to stay overnight there, but after
5 ½ hours, I was emotionally wiped out. I kissed him and told him
I would see him in the morning, and went out to the car. I called
Betty on my cell phone to see if I could crash at her house; then
burst into tears. I cried all the way there. Joyce (sister) called me
and I had to pull off the road to talk; I could not drive, talk and cry
at the same time! I got to Betty's and she had lit candles and had a
glass of wine out for me, and let me cry on her shoulder for awhile.
I think I needed that cry! I slept well, and it was better today. I
stopped at Cheri's on the way back to Richfield, and had coffee and
a nice chat with her. John was no better today, but I could handle it
better. We walked over to see Mother; she is handling her situation
better, but still wishes she could live with one of us. I asked Audra
if she thought it was the meds, or just normal progression of the
disease. She thinks it is the latter. I called Sally so John could hear
their voices, and he had tears running down his face, listening
to them. He started to cry when I left this afternoon, but caught
himself. I helped him take a shower, shave and brush his teeth; he
cannot do any of that by himself now. Sally got an email from one

of her friends who was praying for us, and I liked it: " I am praying for your parents today. The Lord has brought them to mind
several times today. What a blessing to know they are saved. It is
hard to understand how the Lord uses circumstances like these in
a person's life (I'm thinking of your dad here). We can't know what
is really going on in his spirit, but know the Holy Spirit lives there
and is ministering to him. I do know that these things are used
greatly in the lives of those of us who surround the person."

10.07.09   It has been nice to be home for these past two days.
I got a taste of what it will be like in the winter: Tuesday was a
rainy day, so I had to be inside all day. I got a lot of business stuff
done, i.e., insurance, bills, etc. Gene P. came over in the afternoon
and we had a cup of coffee and a nice visit. I watched a couple of TV
shows in the evening, and talked to Joyce (sister). Wednesday was
a nice fall day; I worked in the gardens and enjoyed that! Nancy
and Cheri came over for lunch and we had a nice visit here. I thank
God for three wonderful sisters. Went to prayer meeting tonight,
and was glad I went. My mind is so full of John, that sometimes I
wonder what it will be like when he is really gone. Susan and Roger
went to visit him yesterday, and Nancy came to see him while they
were there. He was confused, and would not stay seated in one
place. I had a call from Richfield tonight that they had found him
on the floor, "in a position like you would be in a hammock" in a
wing, not his, of the place. The caller said he did not seem to have
fallen, was just lying there. She said he is bumping into things,

walls, people, etc. as if he can't see them. I noticed the last few times we have been walking together, he bumps into me, like he can't walk straight. They had called earlier today to ask if it was ok for him to meet with one of the therapists; I asked if it would be Linda, and they said yes, so I agreed.

10.08.09   Had a good Bible study session on Babylon this morning. One of the members came up to Kris and me afterwards, and had some encouraging words for us as leaders; that was refreshing! Gale was at church, so we went out for a quick lunch, and got caught up on the last couple of weeks. I picked Louise up and took her for her flu shot, and grocery shopping. We got to Richfield about 2:00, and left about 5:00. I had opportunity to talk to Audra, and then to Linda (therapist). John is really in bad shape; I just wonder if it is the meds reacting weirdly in him. I had to help him with everything he did while we were there: urinate, brush teeth, wash hands... He did not know how to do anything. We sat outside for a little while, and he kept trying to move things, even the cracks in the sidewalk. He is very unsteady on his feet now, and almost misses the seat when he tries to sit in a chair. Linda said they would try to help him cope, but the damage is irreversible. She was comforting, in that she assures me of how much the staff loves him, and wants to help him. She also cares about my feelings and how I am taking care of me.

He did not talk much, and when he did, it seemed to be about the railroad. He remembered Susan and Roger coming Tuesday, also remembered Doug coming. He knew Nancy had come, too, but had to be prompted to remember her name. He is so restless; cannot stay in one place for long. I think he was glad I brought his mother to visit, but after a while, her constant chattering got on his nerves. Poor Joe (administrator) was stuck with her for about half an hour; he is so gracious!

10.09.09   Good day at home; got a lot done, but not all that I need to do! I worked in the yard for about four hours, and quit for lunch. Got tired by 3:30 and was ready to come in! Hope to make applesauce tomorrow. Had a call from SP (Stewart Payne is the name of John's bldg; I remember it by the golfer Payne Stewart!) telling me that John had fallen. He did not get hurt, but I guess his shuffling way of walking doesn't help. I am thinking that his lying down in the hall the other evening was a result of falling as well.

10.10.09   Roger called this morning and offered to come make applesauce with me. How nice; it was fun doing it together. I got several more tasks done around the house and yard, and then Roger came back for a steak dinner with me. (Sue is at a horse event in Georgia) He is a one in a million son-in-law! (So is Chip!)

10.11.09   Decided last night to go see John after church, so I worshipped and then to Sunday School. I went by to visit Kris and Tom; he is in a lot of pain from the rod in his leg. Then on to Richfield, arriving about 1:00. He looked pretty good; it is hard to believe he is so demented, just looking at him. He doesn't focus; he kinda looks at your neck when trying to talk to you. I got his laundry put in the machines, and we walked over to see Mother for a little while. He stumbled several times, almost knocked me down once, falling against me. He walks off in all directions, cannot walk a straight line. He doesn't seem to see curbs, almost fell a couple of times tripping on a curb. We went back to his room and I turned on a football game for him. He fell asleep on the bed, and I was doing a crossword puzzle, when Linn and Jim came to see him. She had told me this morning in Sunday School that she would go with me to see him anytime I'd like her to come along. We don't know them very well, but I really like both of them. I am not sure John knew who they were. He woke up and sat on the bed, almost incoherent. Linn was great trying to communicate with him. Turns out she had us on her heart and mind for awhile, and even had a "song" for him that came to her. She felt that God was telling her how much He loves John! I asked her to send me the words, and she agreed to. He pooped in his pants while they were there; the smell was terrible. Two of the CRNs came in and cleaned him up, and we went into the sun room and visited while they were helping John. They left and John just wandered around as I put his laundered clothes away. We visited with the next-door resident and his daughter Mary a few minutes before dinner. I had planned to leave when he went in to dinner, but about the time I was getting him seated in the dining room, two more couples from the church came to see him. We left him in the dining room to eat, and went into the sun room to visit. After about 30 minutes, I went to check on him, and he had only eaten a small jello salad, and was poking his spoon onto the place mat. I helped him eat some of his meal, and then he sat with his company and me for awhile. He was unable to communicate, but seemed glad to see them. I am amazed at how our church family continues to come see him, as bad as he is getting. One friend at church told me they had gone to visit him, and he was really antsy, eventually asking them to leave. I got home at 7:20 PM, and feel emotionally wiped out. John said as we were leaving, that he is going to get better and come home.

10.21.09   I went to Columbus October 15–20 and had a great time with the Ewans. I went by to see John before leaving; he seems to get more vacant every time I see him. I am getting calls about his falling down often; they are required by law to let the POA know about falls. I stopped to visit him on the way home from Columbus, and was shocked at how bad he is now. He was asleep in his big recliner in his room, so I did not wake him up. I needed to do his laundry (three loads since Thursday's!) and stepped into the hall and met Linda (occupational therapist) who asked me to come to her office. We sat down and she quietly and gently told me that she did not think he has much time left. He is declining very rapidly, and based on her experience, he will not last long. I cried at first, but then told her that we were ready; this was not a life, the

way he is living now. She said he has gone through stage six, and
I asked if he had exhibited any of the stage seven characteristics.
She said no, not yet; stage seven is when he cannot do anything
at all for himself, like a "vegetable" state. She again talked about
how well both of us have handled this disease, and how she and
Audra are determined to keep him in Stewart Payne, and not have
to go to the nursing home building. I pray he goes before that. We
talked about how we know he will be with God, in a better place,
and that this life is not what we want for John. I felt punched in
the stomach, but thanked her for telling me. I said it has been as
if a sword of Damocles was hanging over our heads, not knowing...
We walked back to his room together, and both of us tried to wake
him up, but he did not open his eyes. He smiled once, and when I
asked him if he wanted to walk outside to go see Mother, he just
mumbled. I told him to stay asleep; that I will go visit her, and will
return. I took his laundry and put it in three washing machines
and left to walk over to see Mother. We visited for about 30 minutes, and when I got back, he was up and messing with the handles
on his chest of drawers. He could not talk, just made a few words,
but no sense. I pointed to a picture of Susan and Roger and asked
if he knew who that was, and he said, that is Susan. Other than
that, nothing else he did or said made sense. He kept his right hand
cupped, and was "eating" out of it with his left hand, even simulat-
ing chewing something. He cannot walk well any more; just takes
small shuffling steps, and is unsteady. He cannot eat by himself, he
needs help, but even then, he more often dumps the spoon out on

his plate, and puts the empty spoon in his mouth. The activities director said that she left Friday afternoon, and returned Monday morning, and could not believe how much he had deteriorated in just two days. She said the volunteers could not take him to chapel any more: he needs one on one attention. So I plan to leave our church after early service, and go to Richfield and take him to chapel there. He stayed with me to do the laundry, but did not act as if he knew what we were doing. He keeps trying to pick up everything, including trash cans, staff clipboards, etc. I called Sally and Susan to let them know how things were, and came on home. I called Louise to let her know I was home from Ohio, and told her he was not doing well, but did not tell her what Linda had said. No need for her to fret about that. I called my sisters to tell them. and my friend Joyce. and Brenda. I feel lost, but comforted; so many are praying for both of us. I spent most of this morning on the phone with HughesNet (lost internet connection; will be awhile for a tech to come fix), insurance co., doctors' offices for bills that came but had not been submitted to insurance, SSA (still having trouble, although they have agreed they owe me and that I did not work in 2007.) Went to church for prayer meetings, and was so blessed just being there with those loving and caring friends.

10.22.09   Kris led Bible study almost by herself today; did a nice job of it. I tried to add points as I saw fit. I stopped at Cheri's on the way to Richfield and we had a nice visit. I got to John about

2:00, and Pastor Mark was with him. It was a shock: he was in a
wheelchair. He could not hold his head up, so never would make
eye contact. He could not make sense talking. He doesn't know to
hold his feet up when you are wheeling him around, but we did go
outside and enjoy the beautiful day. He has to have someone feed
him; Joe fed him lunch today. I left at dinnertime, to take some of
Mother's clothes from Cheri's to her. I did not stay since it was her
dinnertime, too. I feel rather numb, sometimes just want to cry for
him. I can see that it would be a blessing for God to take him on.

10.21.09   Email from Audra:

> Just wanted you to know, Dr. Raza was in facility today and saw
> John. He is decreasing the depakote to 125mg only at bedtime.
> He is wanting to see if that might be causing John to have
> the psychomotor retardation movements. We will be doing
> labs(blood tests) on Monday. I will let you know results of labs
> and also if any change with the depakote.
>
> Have a good evening!

10.25.09   Was glad to have some time at home, to clean house,
work in garden, etc. on Friday through Saturday I was studying for
the Precept lesson on Friday morning, and one of the scriptures
in the lesson was from Zephaniah 3:17: so good for John in his
condition! "The LORD your God is in your midst, a mighty one who
will save; he will rejoice over you with gladness; he will quiet you

by his love; he will exult over you with loud singing." I called Nigel
Friday morning to wish him a happy 18th birthday, and referred to
the verse, and started crying. After we hung up, I cried and cried
for John. It was a cloudy day, but God opened up a window in the
clouds for a ray of sunshine to come through, reminding me that
He is in control, and He loves us.

Went back to see John after church Sunday morning, and took him
to chapel there. He slept almost all the way through the service,
which was a good one. Most of the congregation was in wheelchairs. He is hard to push, because they cannot put him in one with
feet rests or he may fall while getting up. He cannot remember to
keep his feet up, and will accidently "brake" while I am pushing.
He had to go to the bathroom while I was there, and I was trying
to help him sit on the toilet, help wipe him, and get his "diaper" on.
He is so unsteady, he fell down on the floor several times. I am not
strong enough to pick him up, and he could not understand that
he needed to grap the safety bars to pull up. It took about 10–15
minutes, and I was sweating and exhausted by the time he had his
pants on again. I had told Louise I would pick her up and bring her,
but I realized when I took him in to lunch that he needed me to
feed him, bite by bite. The helper had four residents who needed
help eating, and so I stayed to feed John. He ate about half his dinner; having to be fed, and the drinking glass held for him. Vickie
and Melvin came in as he was saying he did not want any more
to eat. So we went out on the patio; it was a nice day. Mike and

Rita came shortly after, and we enjoyed the visit. John fell asleep
several times. As they were leaving, two more couples from our
Sunday School class came in, and stayed for the afternoon. They
were all so kind and so helpful to other residents who came out and
sat down with us. I am continually amazed at the church family
and all their visits and cards. Their prayers are lifting me up to be
able to live through this valley. This season is so beautiful, that I
just rejoice in our Creator God!

10.27.09   Went to Blue Ridge Parkway and Peaks of Otter
lodge for lunch with Gale and Waylon and other friends from
church. Beautiful day, and great company. Had a couple of calls
from Richfield about John. I had emailed Audra to see about taking John off all his meds, as they may be the culprit in his rapid
decline. I went back on the forum for LBD caregivers to ask what
they thought, and am waiting for responses. Audra is checking
with Dr. R to see what he thinks about this suggestion.

10.28.09   Ran errands before going to see John today;
stopped to visit for a little while with Tom and Kristen, and got to
Richfield about 11:15. Audra got Dr. R on the phone, so I could ask
about the meds, and he agreed to stop them. I asked if he possibly
built up a resistance to them, and he said no, not with this disease.
But the disease reaches a point where the meds do not help. So he
goes off the four he is on for dementia, and will stay on the Lipitor.
It is odd how one couple from church visits him and talks about

what a great visit they had, and another tells me he was unable to
hold his head up or communicate! I sat with him at lunch, and he
was able to eat a BBQ sandwich, but could not handle a spoon. So
I fed him some of the vegetables and his dessert. Cheri came over
and sat with us for awhile. He did not remember her being there
when I asked him about it later. Pastor Stan said he was there this
morning, and when he came in, John called him "Pastor." I went by
the funeral home today and made arrangements for both of us. We
will be cremated and then have a memorial service at the church. I
wrote up some facts about John for his obit, and sent them to Sally;
she agreed to write it for me.

10.30.09   Did yard work yesterday and today, still more to do.
Audra called to let me know that John fell again, trying to stand up
from his wheelchair. He was not hurt, but it is happening too often.
They are not staffed to be able to watch him all the time. He doesn't
know he cannot stand alone, and his limbs are so stiff, they have a
hard time getting him to sit, and it is difficult to help him stand up.
I could not care for him here. Later, I had a call from Joe (Administrator of John's bldg.), asking me if I could pay to have someone
sit with him 12 hours a day, 7 days a week. I said, no, I cannot afford
that! I guess I can do it myself, or bring him home and take care of
him. I asked about giving him a seat belt but they are not allowed
to restrain residents in assisted living. He said he and Audra will
talk and call me back if they come up with any alternatives. I called
Audra after crying for awhile and talking to Sally and to Nancy. I

asked her if we could put John on some other kind of med. that would help him stay still better. They are not allowed to restrain either by chemicals or physical means. She did call the doc, and he agreed to put him back on the klonopin. hope that helps. Then Joe called and asked if I would pay for someone to come stay Sunday noon - 7pm. I called Kris and asked if she would get Sunday School class members to come cover that timeframe, and she readily agreed. Linda (therapist) called, and was comforting; she said at this point, it will not matter to John where he is, assisted living or nursing home. She is guessing that he may last another month, but just a guess. Last call was Audra: they will re-evaluate him Monday to see if he needs to go into nursing home, but she said they will wait until I get back on Thursday to do anything. and my precious Dempsey is sick! Pray God it is not swine flu. Also learned that Cheri and Rafael are putting their house on the market, and plan to move to Charlotte area. This has been a day of bad news!

Roger is coming up for dinner; this morning he helped me plant two dogwood trees he got from Gary. Susan is at a horse event in Lexington this weekend. I may ask if they will go be with John on Tuesday or Wednesday.

Move to the nursing home

11.07.09 John is now in the nursing home section, or as they call it: Recovery & Care Center. I took Louise to see him Friday, and it was the first time she has seen him since he has declined so dramatically. I think she was shocked: she was quieter than usual. He only moved his lips, no sound at all when "talking." I called so the grandchildren could talk to him, and he did mutter to each one of them, "I 'ove 'uu too." He did not eat very much, but is eating enough to sustain him, I guess. I took Louise to the grocery late in the afternoon, then took her back home. I met Nella for dinner; have not seen her in way too long. It was enjoyable; we have known each other for 44 years! She still looks great!

On to Betty's from there, to spend the night, and leave the next morning for our mini-vacation to Sapphire Valley, NC, in the mountains. Had beautiful weather, great food, and a relaxing time. Hiked, swam (indoor pool!) and played miniature golf, read, etc. As soon as we got back to her home, I went to Richfield to see John. I had called Audra twice about the evaluation while we were in NC; I could tell she did not want to tell me that he has to leave the assisted living facility. I met with the admissions person for the nursing home, and got it arranged for Friday. I cried several times, but was able to get control of myself. I hate so much for him to have to leave where he was; they are *so* good to him.

I spent the night at Cheri's, did not get much sleep, and got back over to Richfield by 9:30. They had packed John's clothes for me, and they were so sweet and kind. One of the staff washed his hair for him. I wheeled him over to nursing home about 11, and Audra and Jessica took the clothes and helped me hang them up in his new room. He has a roommate, John, who has MS, but his mind is fine. We did not meet him, but saw him. Evidently he stays outside smoking most of the morning and naps in the afternoon. John did not seem to be aware of the change in location. We met the director of nursing and several of the staff; they seem nice enough. Linda (therapist) came over to see us in the community room; it was good to see her. She is so kind. Others who learned to love him in assisted living said they will visit him. They also told us to come over there once in a while for lunch, and I can wash his clothes there, too!

Susan and Roger came while he was eating lunch; Susan and I hugged for awhile, and I cried a little on her shoulder. We left by 3:00, and it was good to get back home after almost a week. Today I worked outside, painting and raking; a beautiful day. Called sisters and friends to catch them up on the news. Talked to retired pastor yesterday; he had gone to see John, but thinks John did not recognize him. It had been three months since John saw Larry. I found out that there were about eight Sunday School friends who went last Sunday to sit with him. I hope I will remember how much this means to me, and will take time to visit shut-ins after...

Lots of paperwork to do; lots of bills to pay. The new facility is much more expensive, and insurance will not cover it. I am so thankful for John's working at NS with the good retirement package. I have felt pretty good today; working outside is therapeutic. I woke up this morning without that heavy feeling I usually experience. Susan and Roger came up for waffles, and that is always nice. She goes to Phoenix for two weeks Monday.

11.09.09   I can't stop crying this morning. I had a restful day yesterday, church, Sunday School and then home, dinner with Susan and Roger. Felt as if I rested well, but this morning, I called the insurance company to try to straighten out some questions on bills, and they would not talk to me. I have called them a number of times and never had trouble with them; now they invoke "privacy laws"! I started crying after that and cannot stop. I am trying to work on the Bible study lesson for Thursday, and cannot concentrate on it. I hate "pity parties" and I feel like a jerk with all this crying. I think I will work in the garden for awhile and see if that helps; sometimes it is like therapy.

11.10.09   I called my friend Joyce before gardening yesterday, and she always makes me perk up! She listens, commiserates, and prays with me. What a friend! I thank God for her, and for other friends who have carried me through all these days.

When I got to John's room, he was in bed asleep. The CRN said after his shower, he was falling asleep, so they got him into bed about 2:00. I got there about 2:30, and just sat by his bed with him. I took his dirty laundry over to the other building, put it in a washing machine, and walked over to visit with Mother for a few minutes. Her "tape-recording" was going. She was sympathetic about John, but mentioned more than once that she wished she could live with one of her daughters. I finally left, and went back to check on the laundry. I know she cannot remember saying things, so she continually repeats herself, but it does get on your nerves anyway! I tried to get John up when I went back, to get him in his wheelchair, but he pulls against me, and I am not strong enough to get him up. It took two of the staff to get him into his wheelchair. I left at dinnertime, and went to Betty's; we went to the Roanoke Symphony and enjoyed a wonderful concert, and I slept well last night! I took Louise and went back today, after going to a music store and buying a piano! I have been playing with that idea for over three years, and finally decided to do it! We got to Richfield as they were being served lunch. John was asleep in his chair and it was almost impossible to wake him up; he did not eat very much. I tried to feed him, but he had a hard time opening his mouth, chewing, and swallowing. I went out of the room and talked to the head nurse. I told her I do not want feeding tubes; she will be checking to be sure my paperwork is clear on that. I feel such love for him now, in his diminished state; he is so handsome, even in this condition, and I just want to cry when I see him like this. I try to tell him how much I love him by my touch, and telling him, even though I am not sure he understands me.

11.12.09   Heavy rains and flood warnings, so no Bible study this morning, but I went anyway to meet with Ken about the memorial service for John. Doug met with us, too, and we came up with ideas, and they helped me understand what is usual for a service. I want it to be a celebration of John's life. He had asked for "How Great Thou Art", as do 90% of people! Doug and Ken suggested "I Fall on my Knees" which the choir is singing this Sunday. It is beautiful; Ken gave me a CD of it. I told them I may ask Larry to have the prayer, and I plan to ask Stan to have the message, and Doug and Mark to say a few words. Sally had suggested it would be nice to involve Awana somehow, and they had the idea of Ezra doing the sound system, and Alton playing his violin. I am considering having Stan ask if anyone wants to make a comment during the service.

I went to see John after that meeting, and he was sitting up (bed was at angle) in bed, sleeping. I let him sleep awhile, holding his hand. He jerked like a spasm several times. Opened his eyes, but did not seem to focus. I went to see Linda to find out what the rehab could do for him. (They called to see about trying to help him.) She wants him to be comfortable in a chair, but he is too "floppy-headed" to be comfortable in a regular wheelchair. So she got a "jerry-chair" for him. It is awkward to push, having four small wheels, but looks like a lounge chair. Four men from church came to visit him while I was there, and Linda gave them info about this disease, and stated that he is in stage seven of seven stages. They all went into his room, and spoke to him, and he perked up considerably, even laughed. He tried to talk, but the words were unintelligible. After I got him into the activity room for lunch, I left. I did not sleep well last night, and scared myself driving home: I thought I would fall asleep at the wheel!

11.15.09   It was good to be home Friday; I got a lot done: prepared dried apples, organized some of the bills and insurance reports (although I have a stack of them to make calls for explanations on Monday. I want to get all of these paid before year end for tax purposes! Doug and Donny came over Friday in response to my request to get the lawn mower blades sharpened. While they were here, the piano movers came and got the piano in. It looks really nice, and I was able to play many hymns, as long as they didn't have too many sharps or flats! I play very slowly; always did have trouble with the left hand playing. It is worshipful to just sit and play. I was on the phone with SSA for over an hour; they still have not paid me for August and September! I will call RR Retirement Monday to see if they are the hold-up. Then I was on the phone 45 min. with Wyndham, trying to figure out what to do about my points for next year. They had been using my bonus points this year instead of my regular 2009 points, so I was going to lose them Dec. 31. They agreed to continue the bonus points through 2010. Betty came here for lunch Saturday, then helped me move some furniture around, then we went to the Free Clinic fund raiser. I had my blood pressure tested (normal) and osteoporosis test, a little over what is normal. I had planned to go see John today, but I need to see the business office, and stop at one of the doc's offices, so I am going tomorrow, and taking Louise. It was a beautiful day for mid-November, and I went for a long walk, and then sat on the porch and read. I will practice piano this evening. The choir sang "I Fall On My Knees" this morning and it was awesome! I emailed Ken that *yes*, please let's have that at the service for John!

"Today you will be with Me in paradise"

11.19.09   It's over now. The end seemed to come *so* quickly, although sitting there holding his hand in the last hours, listening to him struggle for breath, did not seem to go very fast. I took Louise to see him Monday; he had his eyes closed almost all the time, and he was in his geri chair. He had eaten only a few bites at breakfast, and had slept through his shower. The staff told me that while they were getting him dressed, he opened his eyes and smiled at them. I tried to feed him lunch, but he only ate a little ice cream. He has forgotten how to swallow, and just holds food in his mouth, then chokes on it, and coughs and coughs. Sabrina (RN) told me he had aspirated, and she could get a doc in, do x-rays, etc. I asked her "Why?" and she agreed. Louise discovered that a woman in the next room to John's was a neighbor of theirs when John was a little boy. The woman had heard John trying to breathe, and had prayed for him, although she did not realize at the time that it was "Butch." Her children and John had played together as kids! I asked Sabrina if she was sure it was ok for me to go off to DC with Betty this weekend, and she said, *yes*, you need a break. But she did tell me it was time to bring Hospice in. So when I got home, I called Gary to see if he would be the Hospice volunteer for John, and he graciously and readily agreed. Hospice called me at home Tuesday morning to see if I could meet them at Richfield that day to talk and to sign papers. (Evidently Medicare pays for Hospice.) So I cancelled my lunch plans with Ginger and went there. His breathing had become much more labored, and I asked Sabrina again about my going away. This time, she said, You'd better stay here; it is a matter of days now. So Betty cancelled our trip. No disappointment here; I would have had my mind on him the whole time anyway.

I met with the Hospice representative and the nurse; I signed papers, then the nurse and I went into John's room. She examined him; I noticed his hands were cold (They were *never* cold) and his fingernails were turning blue. She had a hard time getting his blood pressure. I asked her if I should plan to stay the night, and she said, "Yes, it is now only a matter of hours." They moved him into the "pallative" room: the Hospice room on the floor, a very nice room with room for family and friends to sit comfortably. When I got into the room, holding his hand, I called Cheri, crying, and asked if she could come. She said, "I will be there in a few minutes." and she was. They brought us food, and were so caring and loving. Shortly after Cheri arrived, and I cried on her shoulder, even though I was ready for him to go to the Lord. In a few more minutes, into the room came Roger, Joyce and Pat! I could not ever describe how I felt when I looked up and saw Roger—to me at that time, he looked like a pillar of strength. and he was. Of course, I was so happy to see my guardian angel Joyce and her Pat; she has been a rock for me through all of this. All day, members of the staff from the assisted living home, including Joe, were coming to see him. I am not sure he knew it, but if he did, he had to feel very loved. There were tender touches, kisses, tears, and loving words. Joe prayed with us; Pat prayed before they left. Cheri and Roger stayed with us 'til the end. That meant so much to me; I will never forget their care and love for us both. During the day, I called Sally and the kids, and Susan in Phoenix, and had them say a few words in his ear. I talked to him, too, telling him how much I love him, and what a good husband, dad and Bumpa he had been. No response, although Cheri and I thought something passed over his face while Susan was talking to him.

More food was brought in from the assisted living staff. The night shift group from Stewart Payne started coming in to see him. That was so touching; you would think they see so many people, one man would not matter. But they truly love him; he was so sweet to

all of them when he lived there. Joe said his staff loved John
too much!

A couple of times, his breathing changed, and Cheri, Roger & I
sat up straight and thought it was the end. The nurses came in at
midnight, and asked us to step into the hall. Cheri and I had been
commenting over and over about how handsome he still was. In
about three minutes, the nurse opened the door, and called us
back in. When I looked at him, he was gray, and I cried, "He's gone!
He's gone!" and ran to him and kissed and caressed him. and cried.
and cried on Cheri's shoulder and in Roger's arms. But I thanked
God for taking him before he had to suffer any longer. We could
not believe how in that few minutes of death, he aged 20 years. He
looked like a very old man in death. I felt numb, and still have to
remind myself that he is gone... But I rejoice that he is with Jesus
in heaven!

We left then, Roger to get home just before 2 AM, and Cheri and I
to her house. I slept about four hours, and got up early to go back
to Richfield and pick up the rest of John's things. I went by to see
the guys in Stewart Payne and they had gotten the news. I made
several calls, and received several on the road. I felt exhausted,
but wired, knowing what all had to be done in the next few days
to be ready for Sunday's service. I stopped at Louise's appointment, after calling Joyce, Betty and Becky to hold me up in prayer
while I told her. I picked up a photo album that I had taken to John,

walked to her door, and as I was knocking on the door, I started crying again. So when she opened the door, she knew. We hugged and cried together, and she said, "It is for the best; he would not have wanted to live like this." Answered prayer, thank you, God! I called Billie (her sister) for her, and she commiserated; said she will bring Louise to the church Sunday.

Betty called and said she would come out and help me get the plans and to-do's in place, and it was great to have her here. I had many phone calls and emails, because Sonja had sent out a church email letting them know he was at the end. I sent her the news, and she distributed that email out to the church family. I began immediately to get phone calls and emails; what a wonderful church family we have!

Sally called Wednesday afternoon and told me she would come Thursday; what welcome news! I was so happy and surprised that I cried on the phone! I rode with Roger to pick Susan up from the airport Wednesday evening; she cut her business trip short to come home. I was so thankful to have both girls here during this time of bereavement. I went on to church Thursday morning, and after meeting with Mark and Stan, I went into Bible study. Kris led the session; it was hard to keep my mind on the lesson. Neighbors (Mary Jane and Ann) came by Thursday afternoon, bringing food. By the end of the week, we had so much food, we could have fed an army. I am so grateful for the outpouring of love and concern from friends! Sally stopped in Roanoke to visit Louise for a little while, and when she got on the road to come here, she got stuck in traffic caused by an accident on 220. Sheri L came by (from Susan and Roger's church family) with more food. Gale and Waylon came by, with more food, then Barbara and Gene. We continued to receive friends and food for a couple of days. Chip came Saturday and brought the kids, so we had a good time eating and talking, and just enjoying each other. I am so tired, even though I am sleeping ok. I guess I am just worn out from all we have been through the past few months, and especially the last few weeks and days. I am sure I am emotionally tired, too. Roger's parents came in Saturday through Monday for the service; I really appreciated that, especially since they are coming back again for Thanksgiving. Bob and Ginny drove down from Cleveland and were with us Saturday night for dinner, and again Sunday for service and afterwards at the house. Cheri, Rafael, Tony and Nancy came to the service, and Nancy and Cheri came back to the house afterwards, too. I am amazed at all the food people are bringing; but very thankful since there are so many folks here.

I am excerpting part of Sally's take on the service itself:

> We had a lovely day yesterday. Chip, Dempsey, and I went to church with my mom; the boys went to church with Susan and Roger. Mom was surrounded by loving people expressing concern for her, and I am always amazed by the love and friendli-

ness shown to me each time we are there, even under normal circumstances. We came home and ate lunch, then went back to church about 2 pm for the memorial service. Mom cried at the doorway when she looked into the sanctuary and saw Dad's photo up on the big screens. It was wonderful to see my aunts and other relatives. Mom had a hard time getting into the sanctuary to sit down because there were so many people that wanted to speak to her and give her a hug. They played the slideshow that Nigel had made of photos from Dad's life, and then they had a wonderful service. Mom had chosen great hymns and scripture that spoke of God's sovereignty and majesty. Their former pastor did the first prayer, then the other pastors each had something to say about Dad. They spoke lovingly and warmly of his friendliness and energy and zeal to serve, and of his love for Mom and Susan and me and his grandchildren. The pastor's message was based on the story of Lazarus and how his sickness brought glory to God. It was a very moving service, and honored Dad's memory and really emphasized the Gospel message of hope.

The choir was huge....even bigger than it had been in the morning worship service. One of the choir members told me it was a real tribute to Dad to see how many people came to sing for his service.

Then we stood in a receiving line and spoke to about a jillion people. I'd not thought about it ahead of time, or I would have said something to prepare the kids! But they did really well. It was amazing to see all of the people that had come to pay their respects to Mom and Dad. When I saw their neighbors from when they lived at the lake, I almost cried, because it was such a surprise to see them again, as well as another neighbor from that area. I hope they were touched by the message and spirit of the service.

But as usual with such events, I didn't get to talk to everyone that I'd wanted to. Jill, Scott, and Meghan stayed a long time at the reception, waiting for the crowd to thin out, and Mom really appreciated their coming. My aunts came back here to the house afterward, and it was great to be with them. Chip and I used to visit them before we had kids, so we had fun catching up. There was a lot of laughter. I'd cried in the morning worship service (I laughed and cried at the same time when the first song the choir sang was that "hope will rise as we wait upon the Lord, we will wait upon the Lord, we will wait upon the Lord." I always associate that song with Steve B. and the rock band, so it was almost surreal to hear it done in a contemporary pop kind of version—you're probably used to that kind of thing at your new church?) but I didn't cry in the afternoon. I was so conscious of how much love and respect these people had for my dad. Very heart-warming!

Widowhood

11.29.09   I now feel like a widow; not sure when the tide
turned, but realization hit me yesterday.

I feel like half a person. I guess I will get used to it. I am still "tired
and wired" and have a hard time concentrating on anything. It
was great to have Sally and the kids here until Friday morning; the
house was so empty after they left. I went by the church to drop off
some dishes, and found that there were four huge flowers/plants
there. I then met Betty for coffee; we had planned to hike, but it
was cold and very windy, so we just met for coffee. From there, I
went to Nicki's and enjoyed playing with their little boys and
having dinner with them. Saturday, I stayed busy all day; got a lot

done. Moving my sewing room from basement to one of the guest bedrooms; Roger and a couple of college students helped move the heavy furniture today. I am going to church this evening for a Thanksgiving service; need to be with my fellow believers! Joyce and Pat treated me to brunch this morning after church.

Emails between Ginny and me:

> Hi Ginny and Bob,
>
> Thank you so much for coming over the weekend; that meant so much to me. It was so good to see you, and experience yet another milestone in life with you. I hung the framed poem in our bedroom; Susan went in there to read it yesterday, and came out crying. It is a beautiful sentiment!
>
> I received a nice card and note from young Bob. The outpourings of love and sympathy are wonderful. I thought yesterday, "I am a widow." and it was such a weird realization. Almost like I am not the same person I was, and I guess I am not.
>
> I plan to come to Columbus Dec. 22 'til ? If weather permits, and you all are not out of town, maybe I will try to come up during that last week of the year.
>
> Love,
>
> Anne

You're right about being a different person. I think we all are,
having been a part of John's life. I have been so inspired by
the faith you and John have displayed and *lived* through the
years. John was doing God's work even in the doctor's office
when he wrote that sentence. It will be unknown how many
people that sentence will inspire. The outpouring of people at
his service is a testimonial to *both* you and John. I'm so glad that
you have Susan and Roger right there and your church family.

We would love to have you here for however long you can
stay anytime, but the Christmas holiday time would be terrific.

Love,

Ginny

11.30.09   It is a cold and rainy day; very gloomy. I have been
edgy all day; starting a task, getting restless before completing it,
and trying to read, cook, clean, iron, play piano, etc. just jumping
from one thing to another. I am so sad, almost depressed, and my
chest has really been hurting me. These chest pains have been
going on for days, really bad at times. I took a prilosec this morning
to see if it would help, then I would know it was just heartburn.
At first I thought it was pulled muscles from moving heavy items,
then I wondered if it might be pleurisy. Oh well, having had the
EEG in April, I am not worried about it being my heart. Just
heart ache...

12.01.09   A beautiful, *cold* day today; full moon visible when I got up at 6:15 this morning. Still not sleeping well; keep waking up in the night. Trying to study for the Revelation class this Thursday, and getting frustrated with inability to understand the questions in the lesson—on the timing of the Rapture. I am beginning to think with all the different opinions on it, that we are not supposed to *know*, just to be ready.

I had called the church Friday to see if there was a need for a 9-foot Christmas tree; Doug responded that Yes, they could find a use for it. Then I found out later from Joyce that the "decorations" committee was struggling with not wanting to pay big $$ for one! So hopefully someone will come pick ours up today and put it to use. I moved the box about 80 feet to the door, but it is *heavy*. Hopefully a strong man will come to get it!

I wish I were not so tired. Brenda told me last night that it took about a year for her mom to regain her strength and energy after her dad died. I am lethargic as well as lack of energy, i.e., tired and lazy! Queasy stomach, and hurting rib cage, but not as bad as the past few days.

12.04.09   I was pretty sick early the morning of Dec. 3; had trouble sleeping, rib cage hurting badly, and I threw up about 4am. I got up about 6:30 and got dressed even tho I still felt shaky. I had so much to do Thursday: Bible study, lunch with Kris and Marie, errands to run, taking Louise to grocery, etc., piano lesson. I got

to feeling much better after lunch, and turns out the piano lessons

will not start until after holidays. I had asked for prayers for my

time with Louise, and the time went well; she was very apprecia-

tive of my running her around. Betty and I met for quick supper at

Panera, and I got home much sooner than expected.

12.05.09   I have realized how weather affects my spirits; two

lousy days this week, and my emotions were ragged. Nice days, and

I am much more myself. Susan and I went in to Rocky Mount this

morning, got haircuts, shopped, and had lunch; very enjoyable!

Mary Jane and I walked for about 5 miles this afternoon; that

was energizing for me: I came home and worked on getting some

Christmas decorations up. Susan brought up a big box of greens

from their garden, and I washed them, saved some to take to Lou-

ise, and froze some. She and Roger planted a Crimson King Maple

in the yard in memory of John. I hope it lives and grows to be a big

shade tree! I have had several calls and emails from friends want-

ing to do lunch or go to dinner; what a wonderful group of friends I

am blessed with!

12.10.09   Betty and I had a nice trip to Myrtle Beach De-

cember 6–9; chilly and cloudy, but enjoyable anyway. I always am

sad driving in to church on Sunday mornings, but this one was

harder than usual. I had several "cries" on Sunday; the choir sang

the beautiful anthem they had sung at the memorial service, and that brought on more tears. After we got to the condo at the beach, Betty went to swim, and I stayed in the condo, and had a good cry. I miss him so much; remembering how much we enjoyed doing things together. Today I took Louise to Stewart Payne, so we could thank them again for taking such good care of John. She took a couple of her delicious banana breads; I hope they enjoy them. We then visited Mother for awhile; so sad to see how blank her mind has become. I met Bonnie W. for lunch after Bible study and a doc visit (routine), and that was so enjoyable; I love that Bonnie! I met Barbara R. for dinner, and that was enjoyable, too! She gave me an ornament of a "strong angel"—I hear that word describing me so often; I do not feel strong! Barbara told me she knew several women had been watching me, to learn from me how they might handle this situation if and when they find themselves in it. I hope I have honored God in my response to the illness and death...

From Pastor Kevin:

Sally,

Know our prayers are with you, mom, and the entire family during this time in your lives. While there is big part of you that will miss dad, I was so thankful and blessed to hear how you shared the news of dad's passing with Julie. You are so right. Dad has been welcomed into the Lord's eternal family. What an unreal, incredible moment that must have been for him and now for all of you as you process dad's life, faith, and eternal security.

I praise God for your dad, Sally. He was a wonderful example
of a man after God's heart. He richly blessed my life and his
commitment to the Lord's church and to ministering to others
set him apart from many. I still think of him, even when he was
sick, going and serving the little one's in the faith through Awana.
What an example! He truly understood what God had done for
Him through Christ and made sure the rest of us were well aware
of that by how he lived. His words to the doctor, late in life, will
always ring in my ears. He knew he was a child of God. He knew
where he was going when he died. He is now there. Thank
you Jesus!

Thank you for sharing your family with me. I will miss you
dad but rejoice that his suffering has ended and that his salvation has been made complete. Please give mom a hug and a kiss
from all your/her Mountview family.

In Him,

k

Dec. 15; after a thank you for the memorial to FHBC:

Anne,

No need for thank you. You and John have always been
family to us, especially to me. I will greatly miss your husband.
He always greeted and treated me with such kindness and care.
Being with and around him always let me know that there was

someone in my corner, someone who understood, someone who really did care no matter what was happening here at the church. Loyalty and friendship are becoming harder and harder to find. Your husband was a shining example of both. It did not take but a few seconds to see the light of our Lord shining through him. He was a gift to all that knew him, even me seeing him only here and there.

I felt very blessed back in the summer of 2008 to see you all while on vacation in North Carolina. I remember talking and laughing with John as we walked the sand dunes and watched the kids play. Something I will always hold onto. Thank you Anne for allowing me to share life through the years with you both and your family. I look forward to seeing you again next week.

In His Love,
    Kevin

I have joined the Apples of Gold widows' ministry at our church and will be attending a luncheon with them tomorrow. I am looking forward to it. I still have to remember that I am a widow. I have been busy the past week, spending too many hours on the phone with medical bills, insurance and Railroad Retirement people! I am just giving up on trying to straighten out the missing three months of RR/SSA payments; I am tired of arguing with them.

I did get one of the insurance payments from a policy we had
bought years ago, and re-invested the money into another insur-
ance/annuity instrument for myself, with Sally and Susan
as beneficiaries.

Chip's dad Jack had a heart attack, and we are now praying for him.
He is to undergo surgery in a few days.

01.01.10   Now that the holidays are over, and it is a new year,
I am ready to face the future, knowing that I have committed my
widowhood to God. Christmas at the Ewans was bittersweet—a
great time with them as usual, but how I missed John! Especially
as we went into the church for the Christmas Eve service, remembering all the times we have been there together. The kids had each
written a "letter" remembering "Bumpa" and reading those was
another time for tears. We watched a 2007 Christmas morning
video, and there John sat, on the sofa, smiling and watching the
kids open presents; I cried a lot seeing that! Nigel sat beside me and
put his arms around me, comforting me. I cry as I remember
it now...

I am still having lots of pain in my lower rib cage and sternum; I
looked up "pleurisy" on the internet, and it sounds like that may
be my problem. Since this has been going on for months now, I
think I will make a doc appointment soon. We had 15 inches of
snow on Dec. 19th, and I got out and shoveled a pathway to get the

car out for Sunday morning. I enjoyed shoveling, but am paying
for it now. My lower back hurt terribly all week afterwards, and
still is not normal. I even tried to cross-country ski, but the skis
kept crunching through the snow instead of gliding. I missed John
then, too; we used to do that together in Ohio. I went on into Rocky
Mount Sunday morning; Betty met me at church. Most of the area
churches had cancelled services, but we had the 11:00 service, and
I was so glad I went. She and I went on to Roanoke and had lunch
at Panera. I tried to go visit Louise, but her apartment complex
was snowed in so deeply, I could not find a place to park. I stayed
at Betty's overnight and left for Columbus Monday morning. That
cut an hour off the seven-hour trip, and the trip went fine. Roads
had been cleared pretty well. Nigel and I made trousers for him
from a Burda pattern; I will not buy Burda again! Not enough
instructions, and also, we tried to alter the pattern to fit his ultra-
slim body! After hours of work, they fit him perfectly!

My wonderful church family called and emailed to be sure I was
having a good Christmas; what a picture of God's church in action!
So many people have commented on how hard this holiday would
be for me, but it was not hard. I do miss John *so much*, but when
I remember how he was the last week of his life, and where he is
now, I cannot be sad for him. or for me. Sally's friends Chris and
Jeanne both were so solicitous, but just right in their response to
me and to my grief. They were sympathetic, and let me talk, but
when I changed the subject, they joined me in laughter and joyful

conversation. The sad part of the visit with the Ewans was that Chip's Dad had to be taken to Hospice. His heart and kidneys are failing, and he is not a good candidate for surgery. Too sad for the grandkids to lose both grandfathers so close together.

I went by to see Mother on my way home; she had forgotten who John was, and when I told her, she also had forgotten that he had died. Her long-term and mid-term memory is gone. She asks the same questions over and over, so her short-term memory seems gone, too. It is sad to be with her; impossible to carry on a conversation. I went over to John's old building, to wish that staff a Happy New Year, and thank them again for caring for him.

I continue to get notices of memorial gifts for our church, for Voice of the Martyrs, and for Gideon Bibles. One of his former Awana boy's family gave 20 Bibles, bringing the total given to 50! One of his Master Gardener friends gave to the library to buy gardening books in his memory. I called Louise when I got home; she was very nice, happy that Susan and Roger had come to see her the previous day.

I spent New Year's Eve with Susan and Roger, and his parents, nice dinner, and a bad movie about WWII. Came home by 11:15, and lay in bed praying until midnight. I took sleeping pill since I had not slept well for several nights. I still woke up and lay awake for a long time in the middle of the night. The pain in my rib cage kept me awake. Mary Jane and I plan to walk later today; I am glad for a walking partner, to be accountable in my getting exercise. It is too easy to sit down with a book! I am reading two books at a time now: a book on widowhood given to me by one of Susan's friends at their church, and a Paul Johnson history of the world. Between books and piano, I don't think I will get bored being alone. I do want to invite people over for lunches and dinners, but need to plan some meals first. My freezers are full, but not with "company" food! I hope to get all the business finished in the next few days; still outstanding doc bills and insurance stuff. I split one of his life insurance policies in two, for the Jellums and the Ewans, but have not yet received the check. I went ahead and gave them checks, and signed the cards "Love, Mom (and Dad)" for Christmas.

I do not yet know what my pension will be; railroad and SSA are so difficult to work with; I will see what the Dec. bank statement has on it. I got a check from NS pension, payable to me, but not sure if this is it, or partial. I pray I will get all this settled soon; seems like I have spent weeks with all this paperwork and phone calls.

01.06.10   Time drags when you are unhappy... This has been a difficult morning for me. I was with friends most of yesterday, and enjoyed the day: errands first, dentist appointment, then lunch with Ginger, then Renovaré with Joyce and Suzanne, several phone calls with friends after getting home. Woke up this morning (Thank You, God, for several nights of good sleep, using ear plugs!)

not wanting to get up. Lay there and prayed a little while—God, help me pray more meaningfully. My mind will not stay on one thing for long; I guess this is like attention deficit disorder; hope it doesn't last long. I have a long day planned for tomorrow, so I called Louise to let her know what time I would be at her apartment to take her grocery shopping. I told her snow flurries were forecast, so I might need to shop for her instead of taking her out. She responded like a spoiled child, and it made me so frustrated and angry with her. Then I felt guilty, and had a long crying spell, so bad that my eyes are now all swollen. As I screamed and cried, I prayed for help from God. The phone rang in the middle of my crying, and it was Nancy, who of course, was loving and kind, having been through all this with Mother and with Reed's illness and death. So I feel better now, but still out of sorts and with a terrible headache. Being bitter cold outside doesn't help; I will be glad when Spring is here and I can have my "therapy" working outside. MJ and I do plan to walk again today, so that may help.

01.11.10   Doing better, but concerned about my own brain. I feel like it is in neutral. I have to re-read everything, sometimes more than once. When I work on my Bible studies, the questions sometimes don't make sense to me, and I get frustrated. I jump from one activity to another; it takes a lot of discipline to complete a task. I am still not sleeping very well; some nights I sleep ok, many nights I don't. I dreamed about John Saturday night; we were at the Swartzes', visiting! Then I had a nightmare about

terrorists, as if I were in a plane and they were attacking me and
the grandchildren. I was trying to fight them, but my arms and
legs were like they were paralyzed. Debi and Tom had been over
Saturday afternoon, and she was telling me about a dream one of
the young women in the church had about terrorists—maybe I was
reacting to that. Sunday I began teaching the Sunday School class
for Audrey; we are studying Mark. I used Louise as an example
of those content with their level of faith, who may be lost. When
I saw Louise last Thursday, we went to the grocery, then I tried
to talk to her about her faith. I ended with saying I love her, and
want to know that when she dies, she will go to be with Jesus and
with John. She said she wants that, too, and will continue reading
the gospel of John, and will think about what we talked about. On
a positive note, I got a call from RR guy Friday evening that he is
asking RR to re-evaluate my pay (or lack of) from last summer, he
thinks they do owe me that money. Praise God. I had given up on it.

MJ and I are still walking three or four days a week, even in these
frigid temperatures! I am glad we both push each other to do it; it
would be so easy to *not* go out. We are going today, and I feel like I'd
rather take a nap!

01.21.10   John would have been 68 today. Wonder what we
would have done today? Susan and I are getting our hair cut and
going out to lunch together; I am glad I have something planned. I
am working on the quilt I am making from his plaid cotton shirts;

it is enjoyable to hold the fabric and "see" him in these shirts. Friends ask me how I am doing, and I can only say, Some days are fine, some are just sad. I am still walking with MJ, and sometimes her husband goes along, about three or four times a week. Tuesday afternoon Renovaré meetings are refreshing and uplifting. I had a couple from church over a couple weeks ago, and plan to have three friends over Sunday after church. It takes effort to do anything; I don't have the energy or desire to do more than read. I am playing piano every day, and keeping the house clean. Now that I am teaching Sunday School, I study the Bible; that is a good discipline to have to prepare to teach! Louise has bronchitis; I wonder if it might go into pneumonia. She still will not make a commitment; I get the impression she does not want to admit that she has sinned and needs a Savior. Even her pastor friend Carol cannot get her to stay on topic when they talk. I wonder if she has ADD.

I need to start preparing her obit and funeral just in case this disease leads to the end for her.

02.22.10 Over three months since John went to be with the Lord. I have to remind myself of that, to get beyond missing him so much. I now remember all the good things, the good times, before his illness. Susan came up last Saturday and after breakfast, we were sitting talking about him. She started crying, and cried for awhile. The next day (Feb. 14) I had the heaviest feeling of loneliness that I have had so far, on the way home from church. I cried for a long time, then later while talking to Sally, she cried. Valentines Day? whatever...

Louise got better from the bronchitis, but I did go to Oakey's and get funeral arrangements made. She still stonewalls me when I try to talk about salvation with her. I continue to keep busy, finished two lap quilts from his old cotton plaid shirts—how comforting. Sally got one, and Susan got a couple of shirts of his to wear. Playing piano, going out with friends for lunch, reading, house cleaning. Have gone to visit Mother a couple of times, and even gone to see the staff at John's old "home." I am sleeping OK now; praise God for that! I am not afraid of being in the house alone; it is comforting to look out the back windows and see Susan and Roger's house. Trying to eat properly, and occasionally have company over for dinner. I went to Cleveland and Columbus end of Jan. for Dempsey's 12th birthday. Went to see Bob and Ginny; nice visit! Then to spend a few days with Sally and family—so nice to be with them!

Betty and I went to Roanoke Symphony to hear Beethoven and Rachmaninoff—a fantastic concert! I had tears running down my cheeks at the end! Met Betty's boyfriend Herb, nice guy. I pray he is right for her, if not, for God to intervene.

03.20.10   This will probably be my last entry. I am in communications with a couple of publishers about getting this journal published. I am doing pretty well I think. Sometimes I feel as if a wave is washing over me, making me miss John so much it hurts. I especially miss him on Sundays. While sitting in church just yesterday, I almost could feel him come sit down beside me, like he used to do after he ushered. I almost put my hand over to take his, like I used to do. Then I got choked up! I cuddle up at night in a chair, with the "shirt" quilt keeping me warm, and read. I am teaching a Sunday School class, and visiting the sick members; going to Bible study, attending prayer meetings, and enjoying friends, here or out. I am so thankful for the Renovaré group; they are still my greatest support. I try to go in every week to grocery shop for Louise, and still pray for God's grace in me to love her and Mother, and get joy from caring for them. I talk to my sisters and my daughters regularly, as well as Joyce, Brenda, and Betty. I thank God for so many loving people. Now I just want to be close to Him and follow His leading as I walk in this path of widowhood.

Appendix:
About Lewy Body Dementia

Lewy Body Dementia (LBD), though less well-known as Alzheimer's disease, is the second or third leading cause of dementia in adults. LBD kills brain cells in the fore-brain (cortex) and in parts of the mid-brain. Small groups of proteins that become clumped together inside brain cells—these are Lewy bodies.

LBD's symptoms overlap with those of those of Alzheimer's, including memory impairment, poor judgement, and confusion. LBD also typically includes visual hallucinations, shuffling gait, and fluctuations in severity of symptoms. The lifespan of LBD patients averages seven years after symptoms begin.

There is no cure for LBD; treatments focus on controlling its symptoms. Care must be taken in prescribing medications, as drugs may sometimes cause adverse reactions. Often, LBD patients will also be diagnosed with Alzheimer's disease.

People with dementia have impaired mental functioning which interferes with normal activities and relationships. They lose their ability to solve problems and maintain emotional control, and may experience behavioral problems such as agitation, delusions and hallucinations.

Lewy bodies are named after Frederich Lewy, the German-American doctor who first described them in 1912. It is not known why Lewy bodies form in the brain.

At this time, there is no definitive medical test that confirms dementia or LBD in a living person, but neuropsychological testing can measure cognitive decline. Lab tests and imaging studies, though unable to clearly diagnose the disease, can be used to rule out possible methods of treatment. Definitive diagnosis of the disease is possible only through an autopsy.

Breinigsville, PA USA
26 August 2010
244320BV00002B/2/P